g.u.m. drops
(GRAMMAR, USAGE, & MECHANICS)

90 Reproducible Worksheets Based around Editing
Passages from Classic Literature

by

Melissa L. Schneider

www.inthethinkofthings.com

5415 Regency Way

Rockford, IL 61114

ISBN 1-933407-06-9

Printed in the United States

of America

Copyright 2007

To the Teacher:

The G.U.M. Drops workbooks were designed to be used as daily supplements. Each workbook is exactly 90 pages long and is roughly divided into 18 weeks. This makes the workbooks ideal to use every day for one semester. However, because the pages continually build upon each other, you can easily adapt the books to fit your schedule by doing more than one page at a time or doing a page every other day. The workbooks are written directly to the student so that they can complete the exercises unassisted. If they do require additional help, there are notes on many of the teacher pages so that you can help them work through the concepts. The number of errors is also included on the teacher pages, which you may or may not choose to share with the student in order to make the exercises easier/harder.

In the Think of Things reproduction policy is as follows:
We grant to individual purchasers of this book the right to make sufficient copies for use by all students of a single teacher. This permission is limited to a single teacher and does NOT apply to any schools or school systems. Copying this book or its parts in any form for resale is prohibited.

Contents

Complete Sentences

A complete sentence has a subject and a predicate.

The **subject** is the part of the sentence that tells *who* or *what* the sentence is about. The simple subject is the main noun or pronoun. The **predicate** is the part of the sentence that tells *what the subject did* or *gives more information* about the subject. The simple predicate is the verb/verb phrase. If a sentence does not have both a subject and a predicate, it is not a complete sentence. It is a **sentence fragment**.

simple simple

The little white cat pawed at my shoelace.

subject   predicate

My favorite shoes.

fragment - no predicate

Run-on sentences occur when phrases are joined (or run together) without any punctuation or connecting words or with too many connecting words.

He is my best friend he lives across the street.

I have a lot of friends and they are good friends but he is my best friend.

Identify run-ons or fragments. In the others, underline the complete subject once and complete predicate twice. Circle each simple subject and simple predicate.

My mom bought a new camera.

The window broke during the storm.

Typed a long letter.

Lillian made a beautiful collage.

The unbearable drought lasted for three long months.

Our favorite dentist retired last week.

The coffee was good and I liked the donuts but the milk was too warm.

Read this passage from _Uncle Tom's Cabin_. Identify any run-on sentences. Make sure each underlined sentence is complete. If it is, circle the simple subject and the simple predicate. If it is not, identify the fragment as a subject (s) or a predicate (p).

<u>The Shelbys lived in an elegant house in Kentucky.</u> <u>Owned a number of slaves.</u> They prided themselves on treating them well. Mrs. Shelby, in particular, did her best to train them in the Christian faith and treat them as equals. It came as a great surprise when her husband announced that he had sold two of their slaves. She began to argue at once, but he told her it was no use. <u>They were deeply in debt.</u> Mr. Haley, a slave trader, was taking Tom and Harry in the morning.

Tom, affectionately known as Uncle Tom, was the Shelby's best hand. <u>He was honest, hardworking, and trustworthy.</u> Mr. Shelby was sorry to part with such a valuable slave. Harry was a young boy of only four years. <u>Was a handsome, entertaining boy.</u>

<u>Harry's mother, Eliza.</u> <u>She overheard the Shelbys talking.</u> Eliza quickly packed some provisions, picked up Harry, and left the house. Stopping by Tom's cabin, she told the other slaves the news. Eliza had decided to run away with her son she asked them to get word to her husband George who worked on a nearby farm. <u>Then she disappeared into the night.</u>

Sentence Types

There are four types of sentences.

All sentences begin with a capital letter. However, the punctuation at the end of the sentence depends on what type of sentence it is.

Declarative sentences are statements. They end with periods.

The girls went on a hike.

Imperative sentences are commands. They also end with periods. The subject, you, is suggested but not directly stated.

Go find them.

Interrogative sentences are questions. They end with question marks.

Is Selena with them?

Exclamatory sentences are full of emotion. They end with exclamation points.

Selena is lost!

Add capital letters and ending punctuation to the sentences below. Identify the type of each one.

the blue paint matched the carpet perfectly   _____

we're going to be late   _____

unlock the door   _____

alicia wore her new coat   _____

are you going on the ski trip this winter   _____

jump in the pond   _____

the tiger is loose   _____

Edit this passage from *Uncle Tom's Cabin* by adding capital letters and ending punctuation where needed. Use all three types of ending punctuation.

Chloe, Tom's wife, urged Tom to try and escape as well.
she asked him, "Why don't you go with Eliza and Harry "
"I can't, Chloe," Tom replied. "If I don't go, someone else will have to take my place. I can bear it just as well as anyone else. besides, Master has always been able to count on me. I won't break his trust now."
Mr. Haley arrived early the next morning When he found out that Eliza had run away with Harry, he was outraged He demanded help tracking them down. Mr. Shelby ordered two slaves to help him. mrs. Shelby encouraged them to do what they could to slow the slave trader down.
after tracking Eliza for several hours, they found her waiting for a boat to cross the icy Ohio River When she spotted the tracking party, Eliza ran towards the river. Mr. Haley saw her and gave a shout. Eliza called out to God, held Harry tight, and jumped onto a piece of ice! Falling and slipping, she continued bounding across the river on the floating pieces of ice. when she reached the other side, she swiftly climbed up the bank They had escaped

Review Time!

Edit this passage from *Uncle Tom's Cabin*. Underline any sentence fragments and identify them as subjects (s) or predicates (p).

Watched Eliza with a scowl. Mr. Haley didn't have time to wait for a boat to take him across the river. he hired a pair of slave catchers to find Eliza and Harry, and then he returned to the Shelby's property for Tom.

Mrs. Shelby was in the cabin talking to Tom and Chloe when Mr. Haley arrived She told Tom that she would do her best to buy him back again. Then Mr. Haley interrupted and growled at Tom that it was time to leave. tom obediently climbed up into the wagon, and Mr. Haley fastened a pair of shackles around his ankles. They slowly rolled away as those left behind wept.

mr. Haley was taking Tom to New Orleans by boat. He hoped to sell Tom for a lot of money. Mr. Haley was a very greedy man

A father and daughter by the name of St. Clare. They happened to be on the same boat. The daughter, Eva, was a charming girl of five years Her generous, compassionate nature impressed everyone who met her. her father was a wealthy, careless man whose life revolved around his only child.

Nouns

Nouns are words that name a person, place, thing, or idea.

Common nouns name general people, places, things, or ideas.

    coach   country   airline   club

Proper nouns name specific people, places, things, or ideas. They are capitalized.

    Coach Mitchell   Egypt   Blue Sky Airlines   Boy Scouts

Concrete nouns are physical. They can be seen, heard, touched, smelled, or tasted.
Concrete nouns may be common or proper.

    Mississippi River   tree   The Beatles   odor

Abstract nouns are things that cannot be seen, heard, touched, smelled, or tasted.
They name ideas, conditions, or feelings.

    time   despair   determination   confidence

Identify the nouns in the first column as common or proper. Identify the nouns in the second column as concrete or abstract.

doctor _____	wind _____
Asia _____	light _____
park _____	fear _____
Dr. Hamaker _____	garden _____
Titanic _____	impatience _____
Super Bowl _____	honesty _____
airplane _____	Mars _____

Read this passage from *Uncle Tom's Cabin*. Circle at least fifteen common nouns. Underline and capitalize the proper nouns.

eva made friends with everyone on the boat, and she took a special interest in tom. She asked her father to buy tom, and mr. st. clare agreed. When the boat arrived in new orleans, tom accompanied eva and her father to their house. tom was deeply impressed by the beautiful mansion and lavish furnishings. He was surprised to see the other slaves in rich clothing. It didn't take long for tom to see that they were used to an easy lifestyle. Indeed, the slaves were just as lazy and wasteful as mr. st. clare himself, and they thought themselves better than other slaves.

The things required of tom were not very difficult. He spent much of his time with eva. She read his bible out loud to him, and he sang songs to her. In time the honest character of tom won the respect of mr. st. clare. tom was made the manager of the expenses. He handled this responsibility much more wisely than any of those before him.

eva helped tom write a letter to his family. He wanted them to know that he had been bought by a kind master.

Capitalization

Here are more words that are always capitalized:

days of the week	<u>S</u>unday
months of the year	<u>S</u>eptember
holidays	<u>L</u>abor <u>D</u>ay
titles of people	<u>G</u>randpa <u>C</u>ollins
people's initials (also marked with periods)	<u>B</u>. <u>R</u>. <u>A</u>dkins
the pronoun "I"	It was more than <u>I</u> could eat.
titles of works	<u>T</u>he <u>C</u>all of the <u>W</u>ild

Proper adjectives are also capitalized. Proper adjectives are descriptive words formed from proper nouns.

<u>B</u>oston store   <u>A</u>pril wedding   <u>A</u>frican wildlife

Abbreviated proper nouns remain capitalized. They are marked with periods.

Captain > Capt.   Monday > Mon.   Mister > Mr.

Add capital letters and periods where they belong in the sentences below.

we are going to a christmas party next friday

my mother and i had supper at a japanese restaurant

drew enjoyed playing soccer for coach j anderson last year

please show me the correct way to fold an american flag

this letter was supposed to be delivered to mrs h long

on independence day i am going to see the fireworks

prof pamela c briggs enjoys eating danish pastries for breakfast

Edit this passage from *Uncle Tom's Cabin.*

Meanwhile, eliza and harry had been helped along by various people until they had reached the safety of a quaker settlement. Eliza's husband, george, had met up with them there. His master was a cold, ruthless man, and george had managed to escape and join his family. Although they faced many dangerous circumstances, the tired refugees finally made it to canada and freedom. They didn't own a single thing, yet they were happier than they had ever been before. With the help of a kind missionary, they started a brand new life.

It had now been two years since that fateful february day when tom was sold. Although he missed his family, those years had been pleasant for tom. eva st clare had only grown more attached to the faithful slave, and he was completely devoted to her. One day when they were sitting in the garden, eva became very serious. She pointed to the clouds

"I'm going soon, tom," she stated. "I've seen angels, and i know I'm going to live with them soon."

Review Time!

Edit this passage from *Uncle Tom's Cabin*.

It wasn't very long before everyone could see the truth in the words eva had spoken. Her skin grew pale, and she lost weight. Some days she hardly had enough strength to stand. The months passed, and eva grew weaker and weaker. Tom continued to care for her, and he and mr st clare rarely left her bedside.

eva gave all of the slaves a curl of her hair. She entreated them to pray every day and to be good Eva also asked her father to give tom his freedom after she died. Mr St Clare agreed.

Eventually the fateful day came. The whole house felt the loss of the bright, happy little girl. Mr. st clare took her death particularly hard. He spent much of his time with tom. Tom was as devoted to his master as he had been to eva. Mr. St. Clare told Tom that he was in the process of freeing him. Tom declared that even if he had his freedom he wouldn't leave until mr St Clare no longer needed him.

The entire household was shocked when Mr. St. Clare died in an accident just a short time later.

Plural Nouns

Plural nouns name more than one person, place, thing, or idea.

You can make most nouns plural just by adding **"s."**

radio > radio<u>s</u>   square > square<u>s</u>   chapter > chapter<u>s</u>

If a noun ends with **"ch," "sh," "s," "x," or "z,"** add **"es"** to make it plural.

wish > wish<u>es</u>   stitch > stitch<u>es</u>   fox > fox<u>es</u>

If a noun ends with **a consonant and then "y,"** change the **"y"** to **"i"** and add **"es."**

family > famil<u>ies</u>   cherry > cherr<u>ies</u>   spy > sp<u>ies</u>

If a noun ends with **"f" or "fe" and makes a "v" sound in the plural**, change the **"f"** to **"v"** and end it with **"es."**   scarf > scar<u>ves</u>   knife > kni<u>ves</u>

Irregular plural nouns don't follow any rules at all.

tooth > teeth   deer > deer   man > men

Collective nouns name a collection of people, places, things, or ideas.

herd   bouquet   litter   tribe

Read the nouns below. Write the plural forms in the blanks provided.

foot _____   enemy _____   flock _____

country _____   woman _____   rash _____

sheep _____   berry _____   life _____

couch _____   roof _____   hoof _____

Edit this passage from *Uncle Tom's Cabin*. Cross out any misspelled plural nouns and write the correct plural nouns above.

mrs St Clare did not have the same compassion for slaves that her husband and daughter had shared. After Mr St Clare's death, she announced that they were all going to be sold at an auction. Mr St. Clare had not yet given Tom his freedom, and Mrs. St. Clare refused to honor her husband's wishs.

A plantation owner named Simon Legree bought Tom and another slave named Emmeline. He owned several propertys by the red river. Legree was a cold-hearted, ruthless man who worked his slaves to death and then bought more. He had made two of his mans, sambo and quimbo, overseers. The overseers had been trained to hate the other slaves, and they disciplined them mercilessly.

When tom arrived at the plantation, he found that Legree's character had influenced everyone on the plantation. The other slaves were selfish and hard-hearted. They didn't help or care about each other. Tom soon began to have an impact on the abused persons. He helped the weaker ones meet their quota and make their meals. He told everyone about jesus.

Verbs

Verbs are words that show action or complete a thought.

Action verbs tell the action of the subject.

Our neighbor <u>waved</u>.   The leaves <u>fell</u> from the tree.

I <u>ran</u> across the field.   Owen <u>tripped</u>.

Linking verbs link the subject to a noun, pronoun, or adjective that describes the subject. They complete a thought. They do not show action.

He <u>was</u> ashamed.   They <u>looked</u> cold.

These tacos <u>are</u> messy.   Missy <u>felt</u> tired.

Helping verbs come before the main verb and help describe the action or show the time of the action.

She <u>might</u> attend the play.   The horses <u>were</u> eating grass.

Dad <u>will</u> tell his favorite joke.   It <u>is</u> raining outside.

Circle all of the verbs in the sentences below. Identify them as action (a), linking (l), or helping (h) verbs.

The worms were wriggling across the sidewalk.

The lasagna smelled delicious.

I am embarrassed.

The baker placed a fresh batch of cookies in the display.

He should have asked for directions.

Mom had driven to the store.

Read this passage from *Uncle Tom's Cabin*. Identify the underlined verbs as action (a), helping (h), or linking (l) verbs.

Simon Legree was not pleased with Tom's performance. While Tom <u>was</u> a very hard worker, he was not the sort of slave Legree wanted. He <u>had</u> <u>been</u> <u>hoping</u> to make Tom his top over-seer, but Tom was too nice to the other slaves. Legree decided to start training him to be mean. One evening he ordered Tom to whip one of his fellow workers. Tom <u>refused</u>.

"I <u>will</u> <u>work</u> day and night, Master," he said, "but I won't whip any men or women. It just isn't right to be so cruel."

Legree <u>was</u> furious! He ordered Sambo and Quimbo to whip Tom until he learned his place.

Tom was left broken and bleeding in an isolated shed. One of the slaves from the house, Cassy, <u>brought</u> him some water and treated his wounds. Cassy <u>had</u> <u>lived</u> on the plantation for many years, and her misery had slowly turned into anger. She hated Legree and had long forsaken any trust in God.

Before Tom's wounds had healed, Legree <u>ordered</u> him back to work. Tom's life <u>became</u> a wearying cycle of toil and pain.

Review Time!

Edit this passage from *Uncle Tom's Cabin*.

One day Cassy told tom that she had decided to try and escape. No one had ever managed to escape from Legree's plantation before, but cassy had a clever plan. There was an empty room on the top floor of Legree's house One of Legree's slaves had died in the room, and now everyone believed that it was haunted. legree himself was scared to death of the room, for his guilt interfered with his reason. Cassy had been stockpiling supplys in that very room. she and emmeline were going to leave the house and run to the marshs at a time when someone would be sure to see them. While Legree and the overseers struggled to free the dogs and get their horses, the womans would circle back through the creek and return to the house. They would stay in the room for a few days until legree stopped looking for them, and then they would escape in earnest at night. Cassy knew that no one would ever think to look for them in the house, and nobody would go anywhere close to the room.

Cassy urged Tom to escape with them, but Tom said he couldn't.

"I have a work to do among these poor souls," he explained. "i just can't leave them now."

Verb Tenses

Verbs tell what happened in the past, what is happening
at present, or what will happen in the future.

Past tense verbs tell about events that happened in the past.

Simple Past - no helping verbs, often ends in "ed"   >   She <u>played</u> tennis.

Past Perfect - uses verb "had"   >   She <u>had played</u> tennis.

Past Progressive - uses verb "was" or "were"   >   She <u>was playing</u> tennis.

Present tense verbs tell about events that are happening right now, in the present.

Simple Present - no helping verbs   >   She <u>plays</u> tennis.

Present Perfect - uses verb "has" or "have"   >   She <u>has played</u> tennis.

Present Progressive - uses verb "is" "am" or "are"   >   She <u>is playing</u> tennis.

Future tense verbs tell about events that will happen in the future.

Simple Future - uses verb "will" or "shall"   >   She <u>will play</u> tennis.

Future Perfect - uses verbs "will/shall have"   >   She <u>will have played</u> tennis.

Future Progressive - uses verbs "will/shall be"   >   She <u>shall be playing</u> tennis.

Identify the complete tense of each verb/verb phrase underlined below.

They <u>are catching</u> lightning bugs.   _____

Joyce <u>will walk</u> home after the picnic.   _____

I <u>have opened</u> the gift from Grandma.   _____

The wind <u>was ruffling</u> my hair.   _____

We <u>shall have finished</u> our supper.   _____

Read this passage from *Uncle Tom's Cabin*. Identify the complete tense of each underlined verb/verb phrase.

On the day that Cassy and Emmeline faked their escape, everything went according to Cassy's plan. Legree, Sambo, and Quimbo looked and looked for the women, but they could find no trace of them. Legree threatened to kill Tom if he didn't tell him where the women <u>were hiding</u>.

"I <u>will</u> not <u>tell</u> you," Tom said. "They <u>are trusting</u> in me."

Legree commanded the two overseers to whip Tom, and he stood by and <u>watched</u>. He threatened and cursed and yelled at Tom, but Tom bore his punishment with patience. He felt a deep peace, for he knew he <u>was going</u> home. Just before Tom fainted, he told Legree that he forgave him.

Legree looked at Tom's unconscious body and walked away. As soon as their master <u>had left</u>, Quimbo and Sambo <u>knelt</u> down by Tom and revived him. They had been touched by his faith and perseverance, and they cried and asked him to forgive them. Tom prayed with the two savage men.

Two days later a man came to Legree's plantation looking for Tom. It was Mr. Shelby's son, George Shelby. Five years <u>had passed</u> since Tom had been sold, and George had come to buy him back.

Irregular Verbs

Irregular verbs do not have an -ed ending in the past tense.

Irregular verbs don't follow any rules at all; they simply have to be learned.

begin > began   eat > ate   dive > dove   sing > sang

Another verb form is the **past participle**. This verb form means past or completed action. In <u>regular</u> verbs the past participle is the same as the simple past tense, but it is used with one of the following helping verbs: has, have, or had.

She <u>danced</u> gracefully.   >   She <u>had danced</u> gracefully.

In <u>irregular</u> verbs the past participle often changes completely from simple past tense.

I <u>chose</u> a sandwich.   >   I <u>had</u> <u>chosen</u> a sandwich.

He <u>drank</u> some water.   >   He <u>has</u> <u>drunk</u> some water.

They <u>hid</u> the present.   >   They <u>will</u> <u>have</u> <u>hidden</u> the present.

The past participle with "had" forms past perfect tense.   I <u>had sung</u>.

The past participle with "has" or "have" forms present perfect tense.   She <u>has sung</u>.

The past participle with "will have" forms future perfect tense.   He <u>will have sung</u>.

Write the past tense and past participle of each present tense verb.

(begin) Yesterday I _____ typing. I had _____ typing.

(come) Yesterday I _____ home. I had _____ home.

(get) Yesterday I _____ a car. I had _____ a car.

(shake) Yesterday I _____ his hand. I had _____ his hand.

(throw) Yesterday I _____ a fit. I had _____ a fit.

Read this passage from *Uncle Tom's Cabin*. Cross out any incorrect irregular verbs and write the correct verbs above.

George finded Tom lying in a shed.

"I have came to take you home, Tom," George said.

"It does my heart good to see you," Tom replied, "but you're too late. The Lord is going to take me home."

Tom was overcome with joy and peace. He died just a few moments later. George wrapped his cloak around the faithful slave and buried him.

The next day Cassy and Emmeline runned away. They ended up boarding the same boat as George Shelby. There was another woman on the boat who was trying to find George Harris. She was his sister. Cassy heared George telling the woman about George and Eliza Harris, and she couldn't believe it. Eliza was her daughter! Cassy had gave up hope of ever seeing her again. George Shelby directed them all to where the Harris family lived, and they had a tearful reunion.

As for George Shelby, he goed home to share the news of Tom's death. The slaves were deeply saddened, but they were overjoyed when George gived them their freedom. While standing by Uncle Tom's grave, he had resolved never to own another slave again.

Review Time!

Edit this passage from *Frankenstein*.

I was stranded with my sled on a large piece of ice. All but one of my dogs had died; the open sea surrounded me. Suddenly I seed a ship! I had thought that circumstance to be impossible this far north, yet there it was. using pieces of my sled as oars, I struggled until I reached the side of the vessel. The crew members, shocked at my appearance, begged me to come on board and be saved. When I finded out they were heading north, i agreed to board the ship.

Due to fatigue and hardship, I fainted with illness. When I had recovered enough to communicate, I learned that the captain had been most attentive to my needs. I introduced myself as victor frankenstein. His name was robert walton. We spent much time talking, and I soon discovered his purpose in sailing to the north pole. Robert was filled with lofty aspirations and dreams of glory. This same trait in myself had leaded only to pain and destruction. I decided to share my story with robert in hopes that it would make a difference.

Subject / Verb Agreement
The subject and verb in a sentence have to agree.

In present tense the verb changes to agree with the subject. If the subject is plural, the verb must be plural. If the subject is singular, the verb must be singular. Most singular verbs end with "s." The singular subjects "I" and "you" do <u>not</u> follow this rule.

> My uncles <u>talk</u> a lot.   My uncle <u>talks</u> a lot.

> I <u>talk</u> a lot.   You <u>talk</u> a lot.

Compound subjects (two or more) use a plural verb when connected by "and."

> My dad and my uncles <u>talk</u> a lot.   My uncles and my dad <u>talk</u> a lot.

If a compound subject is joined by "or" or "nor," the verb must agree with the subject that is closest to the verb whether it is singular or plural.

> Neither my dad nor my uncles <u>talk</u> much.

> Neither my uncles nor my dad <u>talks</u> much.

Some forms of the verb "to be" change form in past and present tense.

> She <u>is</u> funny.   I <u>am</u> funny.   You <u>are</u> funny.   They <u>are</u> funny.

Circle the correct verbs in the sentences below.

My grandma (sit / sits) on the couch. I (sit / sits) on the chair.

We (is / are) going to the mountains. My cousin (is / are) going with us.

Either my cat or her kittens (eat / eats) too much.

Louis and his brother (sell / sells) produce. Louis (sell / sells) more.

Mom (allow / allows) me to go swimming. Will you (allow / allows) it?

Edit this passage from *Frankenstein*. Circle the correct verbs.

My father, alphonse frankenstein, had married a kind, virtuous woman named caroline, whom he had saved from poverty. I (was / were) their firstborn son. When I was still young, my parents adopted a beautiful orphan girl. Her name was elizabeth, and I loved her dearly. We (was / were) very close in age, and our personalitys complemented each other wonderfully. As we grew up, I became very interested in science. I was especially curious about the secret of life. I often thought of the glory i could attain if I could stop all but violent deaths.

I had only one friend His name was henry clerval, and we were as close as brothers. When I (was / were) seven years old, my mother bore another son, Ernest. Little william came next. When i was seventeen, my mother died of scarlet fever. I leaved soon after to continue my education at a university. I missed my family and Henry, but I was eager to further my knowledge of science.

Verbals

Verbals are similar to verbs, but they function as other parts of speech.

Verbals are formed from verbs and have the power of verbs, but they instead function as nouns, adjectives, and adverbs. There are three types of verbals.

A **gerund** is a verb form ending in "ing" and is used as a noun.

> <u>Swimming</u> is good exercise.   I like <u>swimming</u> on hot days.

An **infinitive** is a verb form usually consisting of a verb preceded by the word "to" and may be used as a noun, an adjective, or an adverb.

> It would be scary <u>to ride</u> an untrained horse.

> If you want <u>to write</u> a good book, you must first have a good plot.

A **participle** is a verb form often ending in "ing" or "ed" and is used as an adjective.

> The flock of <u>honking</u> geese flew overhead.

> Miles of <u>plowed</u> fields surround our farm.

Identify the types of verbals underlined in the sentences below.

She tried <u>to sleep</u> on the plane, but she couldn't.   _____

I returned the carton of <u>cracked</u> eggs to the store.   _____

<u>To keep</u> a secret isn't easy.   _____

The mob of <u>cheering</u> fans rushed onto the field.   _____

My mom dislikes <u>shopping</u>.   _____

<u>Gardening</u> is hard work.   _____

Read this passage from *Frankenstein*. Identify the underlined verbals as gerunds (g), infinitives (i), or participles (p).

Among other things I studied chemistry and anatomy. I was so engrossed in these studies that I advanced very quickly and became somewhat of an expert in only two years. <u>Learning</u> absorbed all of my energies, and I finally discovered how to create life. The next step was <u>to make</u> a man and give him life. I decided to make an extraordinary man, eight feet tall and very strong. After more than a year of <u>working</u>, my creation was finished. I gathered my instruments and gave him the spark of life.

His eyes opened, he began <u>to breathe</u>, and his limbs shook. In that moment I was overcome with horror. He was hideous! His shaggy hair, watery eyes, pale skin, and dark lips disgusted me when I saw them move. I fled from the room and lay on my bed, where I fell into a <u>troubled</u> sleep. Instead of something glorious, I had created a dreadful monster!

When I awoke, the monster was leaning over my bed. I ran out of the house, for I was sickened by the sight of my <u>living</u> creation.

Review Time!

Edit this passage from *Frankenstein*. Identify the underlined verbals as gerunds (g), infinitives (i), or participles (p).

My good friend, henry clerval, arrived the very next day I was so pleased <u>to see</u> him that i forgot all about my horrible creation until we arrived at my door. Fortunately, the <u>created</u> monster had left.

Due to sickness and other circumstances, another couple of years passed before I returned home. <u>Returning</u> was bittersweet; my youngest brother, william, had been murdered. He had turned up missing while playing outside, and my family had spent hours searching for him. His body was found the next morning. he had been strangled, and the locket with our mother's picture had been took from his neck.

When I arrived home, I went <u>to visit</u> the place where William's body had been found. Just then, a flash of lightning lit up the sky. In the distance i saw a tall, hideous figure. It was the monster I hadn't seen him in years, but I knew right then that he (was / were) responsible for my brother's death.

Pronouns

Pronouns replace nouns.

An **objective pronoun** replaces a noun that is an object in a sentence.

A **nominative pronoun** replaces a noun that is the subject of a sentence.

Ken and Wade washed the truck. They washed it well.

A **reflexive pronoun** refers back to a noun or pronoun in the sentence. Reflexive pronouns include myself, yourself, himself, herself, itself, themselves, and ourselves.

The cat licked itself clean. You will have to do it yourself.

A **demonstrative pronoun** points out a noun without naming the noun. Demonstrative pronouns include this, that, these, and those.

This is an outrage! Thank you for showing me those.

An **indefinite pronoun** does not name the noun it replaces. Indefinite pronouns include everyone, anything, somebody, none, either, all, some, both, many, and most.

Anyone could win the game. Many are doing well.

An **interrogative pronoun** asks a question without naming the noun. Interrogative pronouns include who, whose, whom, which, and what.

Which is your favorite? Whom should we invite to supper?

Circle all of the pronouns in the sentences below.

All is not lost. We still have a chance. Everyone must keep trying.

These are delicious. Did you make them? None will be left.

Nora and I are going on a trip to Italy. We paid for it ourselves.

What is the matter? Nobody knows. That is the problem.

Edit this passage from *Frankenstein*. Circle the correct pronouns.

I soon learned that one of our most trusted servants, justine moritz, had been accused of the crime. The locket had been found in the pocket of her dress. (She / Her) ardently denied the charges, but the evidence against (she / her) was too strong. I had no way of proving her innocence; my story was too far-fetched. No one would believe that (I / me) had maked a monstrous man. Despite my best efforts, justine was executed for murder.

I knew that both of these deaths were my fault; i had given life to the wretched creature responsible for taking their lifes. I falled into a deep despair that my dear family couldn't understand They too were hurting, yet I was isolated by the burden of my terrible secret.

I went to the mountains to spend some time alone. While I was there, the monster approached (I / me). I wanted to fight him to the death, but (he / him) pleaded with me to listen to his story. he claimed to have been a peaceful creature before experiencing the rejection and hatred of man. I followed (he / him) to his hut, where he shared his tale

Pronoun / Antecedent Agreement

Pronouns must agree with the nouns they replace.

An **antecedent** is a word being replaced or referred to by a pronoun. The pronoun must agree in number and gender with the antecedent.

If the antecedent is singular, the pronoun must be singular.

> The <u>girl</u> knit a <u>scarf</u>. <u>She</u> knit <u>it</u> for her mother.
>
> My <u>brother</u> went to camp. <u>He</u> will be gone for a week.

If the antecedent is plural, the pronoun must be plural.

> My <u>brothers</u> went to camp. <u>They</u> will be gone for a week.
>
> The girls each knit two <u>scarves</u>. The girls knit <u>them</u> very quickly.

If the antecedent is **masculine** (referring to a boy or man), the pronoun must be masculine. If the antecedent is **feminine** (referring to a girl or woman), the pronoun must be feminine.

> <u>Mr. Watson</u> works at the bank. <u>He</u> has worked there for a year.
>
> My <u>sister</u> is a veterinarian. <u>She</u> paid for vet school <u>herself</u>.

Circle the correct pronouns in the sentences below.

There are three bowls on the table. (It / They) are filled with soup.

That little boy lives across the street. (He / She) is eight years old.

The girl picked out ten books. (She / They) read (it / them) all.

We went camping. We cooked the food (himself / ourselves).

Libby mowed the lawn. (It / They) took (him / her) a long time.

28

Edit this passage from *Frankenstein*. Circle the correct pronouns.

the monster had stumbled away from my house his first night with only a cloak. (She / He) had no knowledge of day and night, land and water, or food and sleep. He passed several days in a forest, where he ate nuts and berrys His first encounters with humans did not go well, so he fled to a place of seclusion. He found an abandoned kennel behind an isolated home in the country, and (he / they) made it his home. A french family lived in the cottage, and he growed to love (they / them). Although he kept himself hidden, he spent a great deal of time watching and learning from them. In time he could understand their language, read, and even speak. eventually he decided to approach the family. Instead of accepting (them / him), they (was / were) terrified and chased him away. Deeply hurt, he fled once again.

The monster had finded some of my papers in the cloak He decided to try and find (him / me). meanwhile, anger and hatred began to grow inside of him. He yearned for revenge against (I / me) and my race, for we had rejected him.

Review Time!

Edit this passage from *Frankenstein*.

The creature comed upon little william by chance. Learning that (he / him) was my brother, the monster had killed him. He wanted to hurt me, for i was his creator and yet had not accepted him.

When the monster finished his tale, he told me he wanted me to create a mate for (him / them). He wanted only what humans enjoyed and yet would not give him - acceptance Once I gived him his mate, he promised they would travel to a remote place and never bother another human again. If (I / me) did not make him a mate, he threatened to continue bringing destruction upon the human race, especially against me and my family. although I hesitated to make another creature capable of such destruction, I decided that i could not allow (him / her) to torment my fellow human beings. I agreed, and (we / us) parted.

in the days that followed, my father approached me about Elizabeth My parents had always hoped we would one day wed, and he thought that our union would bring happiness to the household again. My dear elizabeth and I set the date for the next year.

Apostrophes

Apostrophes are used in contractions and possessive nouns.

Contractions are two words joined together into a single word. Many contractions are made from pronouns, helping verbs, and the adverb "not." Contractions are formed by replacing a letter or letters with an **apostrophe**.

he is > he's   did not > didn't   we will > we'll

The contraction for "will not" changes more than usual.   will not > won't

Apostrophes are also used in **possessive nouns**. Most possessive nouns are formed simply by adding **apostrophe "s"** ('s).

boy's shirt   Will's tent   fireman's coat

If a noun is **plural and ends with "s,"** just add an **apostrophe** (').

pigs' pen   chefs' ovens   twins' closet

Possessive pronouns do not use apostrophes.

our vacation   my laptop   your jacket   his collection

Add apostrophes where they belong in the sentences below.

I cant believe spring is finally here. Its Moms favorite season.

Shes at her grandparents house. They dont live very far away.

This is Alexs room. Its very clean. Well sleep here tonight.

Youve heard of the Northern Lights, havent you? Theyre beautiful.

Im the owner of four ducks. That is the ducks food.

Edit this passage from *Frankenstein*.

In the meantime I set off to fulfill my promise. I told my family that I wanted to travel before settling down in marriage. In truth i needed to do some more studying before I could create a mate for the monster. I wanted to fulfill my obligation so that I could focus on elizabeths happiness.

henry clerval, my childhood friend, accompanied me in my travels. After many months we parted ways. I could finally begin my work. I chose a secluded hut where I wouldnt be discovered and set forth to create life again. What I had accomplished with enthusiasm three years earlier, I now toiled at with disgust. The monster had warned (I / me) that he would be watching, and i had no doubt that hed followed me closely.

Indeed, on the very night I completed his mate, the creature was watching me through the window. The monsters terrible appearance horrified me so much that I couldnt bring myself to give life to another like him. I tore my new creation to pieces

Commas

A comma marks a slight pause in a sentence.

Commas are used to separate items in a series.

> He polished the forks, spoons, and knives.

> The bat flew over my head, behind the tree, and across the field.

Commas are used when people are spoken to directly.

> Jean, do you need some help?

> I'll pick you up at 4:30, honey, after your violin lesson.

Commas are used to set off an **appositive**, which is a word or phrase that renames the noun(s) or pronoun(s) right before it.

> Drew, my older brother, was born in October.

> That hamster, the one sleeping in the corner, is mine.

Commas are used to set off an interruption in a sentence.

> The good news, however, outweighs the bad news.

> This book was, as you warned me, very dull and boring.

Add commas where they belong in the sentences below.

Basketball the best sport ever was invented by Dr. Naismith.

Have you made any new friends Becky?

Kids do you want ketchup mustard and onions on your hotdogs?

I have a hockey game by the way on Tuesday night.

Grandma my mom's mom is arriving Friday Saturday or Sunday.

Edit this passage from *Frankenstein* by adding commas where they belong.

Later that night the monster entered my room walked up to me and demanded to know why I had destroyed his mate. I told him that I refused to carry out my promise.

"Shall every creature have a mate except for me?" he questioned me. "Am I to be left alone while you live in happiness?"

"Leave me monster!" I replied. "I will not change my mind!"

"I will leave you for now, but I will be there on your wedding night," the monster threatened. With those final words, he disappeared into the night.

I shuddered closed the door and set about packing up my things. He had told me that he would come on my wedding night; I resolved to be ready. I would not let him kill me without a fight. I could not stand the thought of leaving Elizabeth the woman I loved alone. I decided I would kill the monster before he could kill me.

An unforeseen event shook me yet again. The body of Henry Clerval my closest friend was found by some villagers. He had been strangled. The monster was punishing me I realized for breaking my word.

Review Time!

Edit this passage from *Frankenstein*.

I returned home with a heavy heart. Elizabeth greeted me with tears in her eyes. She had lost weight sleep and joy over the unhappy events of the last couple of years.

Fearing that the monster might kill another innocent human if (I / me) postponed my marriage, I began to make preparations. I carried pistols knives and other weapons. I was determined to be ready when the monster returned.

Our wedding day arrived, and we enjoyed a quiet ceremony. Afterwards, we traveled to lakeside inn a small hotel on the lake. My thoughts were focused on the monsters threat. If only i could make it through one more night it seemed then Elizabeth and I would be free to live in happiness.

That night I encouraged Elizabeth my new bride to retire to our room. I didnt want her to witness what I knew was coming. I walked around the outside of the inn, searching for any sign of the monsters arrival.

Elizabeths shrill scream suddenly echoed from our room! When I burst in the door, elizabeth's lifeless body was lying on the bed. She had been strangled

Commas

A comma marks a slight pause in a sentence.

Commas are used to separate two descriptive adjectives unless one or both of them is a color or a number.

> We had an exciting, action-packed vacation.

> We spent two exciting days rafting down the river.

Commas are used after a light exclamation or introductory word beginning a sentence.

> Discouraged, I went home.   Oh, I'll have to ask my dad.

Commas are used after a dependent clause, long prepositional phrase, or two prepositional phrases in a row before the main part of a sentence.

> On the way to my aunt's house, our car broke down.

Commas are used to separate two **independent clauses** (complete sentences) joined by a conjunction - AND, BUT, OR, FOR, NOR, SO, YET.

> He made it to third base, and the next batter hit him home.

> Sherry was too busy to drive me, so I took the bus.

Add commas where they belong in the sentences below.

After eating too much ice cream I had an upset stomach.

Well do you want to come over tomorrow?

My brother is taller than I am but not as strong.

The short round clowns weren't as funny as the three tall clowns.

Haven hates to shell peas but I think it is fun.

Edit this passage from *Frankenstein* by adding commas where they belong.

I returned home in despair. My father was unable to bear the horrible unexpected news of Elizabeth's death and he died within a few days. The monster had taken away my family yet I lived. I had never even imagined that he might carry out his revenge in this way!

I vowed to track the monster down and destroy him. This it seemed was what he wanted for he managed to keep me close on his trail without ever letting me get close enough to kill him. For seven lonely months I followed him in hopes of destroying him. He led me north to this very place. That was why I agreed to board your ship only after learning that you were traveling northward.

Thus I ended my story and Robert Walton and I sat in silence.

After hearing Victor Frankenstein's story I felt unimaginable compassion for him. I did my best to take care of him but his health failed daily. He died on my ship, free at last from the trouble caused by his ambitions.

Semi-Colons

A semi-colon marks a longer pause in a sentence.

Semi-colons are similar to commas, but a semi-colon marks a longer pause.

Remember that a comma is used when two independent clauses (complete sentences) are joined by a conjunction - AND, BUT, OR, FOR, NOR, YET, SO. If two independent clauses are joined <u>without</u> the use of a conjunction, then a semi-colon is used and there is a longer pause.

> I enjoyed biology, but I don't like chemistry.
>
> I enjoyed biology; I don't like chemistry.

Another use for the semi-colon is to separate a series in which there is another series within that already uses commas.

> There were crumbs on the floor; dishes, spilled juice, and a box of cereal on the counter; and ants in the cabinets.

Add commas and semi-colons where they belong in the sentences below.

My birthday is next week I got a card today.

Trisha went to the park Leeann went with her.

I left my shoes by the door for they were very dirty.

He opened the mailbox and saw there was nothing inside.

We didn't have any eggs so I went to the grocery store.

The rodeo was very exciting the bull riding was a little scary.

I have a dentist appointment on Thursday a recital softball game and slumber party on Friday and a babysitting job on Saturday.

Edit this passage from *The Black Arrow* by adding commas and semi-colons where they belong.

A bell rang out across Tunstall one afternoon in late spring. The small village was surrounded by forest had a dozen or so houses a great moat-house and a church and was home to a handful of families. The people of Tunstall left their work and gathered around the moathouse to find out why the bell had rung.

The question was answered by Richard Shelton a boy of almost eighteen. Richard's guardian was Sir Daniel Brackley the lord and knight of Tunstall. There was an upcoming battle between the houses of Lancaster and York Sir Brackley needed more men. Sir Brackley had been known to change his loyalties more than once in order to profit personally but Richard Shelton was loyal to his guardian nevertheless.

An old veteran Nick Appleyard was assigned to stay and defend Tunstall with seven men. The rest would join Sir Brackley in Kettley. Richard and Bennet Hatch Sir Brackley's second-in-command explained the situation to Nick Appleyard. As they stood talking an arrow whistled through the air and killed Appleyard. The arrow was completely black.

Review Time!

Edit this passage from *The Black Arrow*.

Richard and Bennet returned to the moathouse. They told the villagers what had happened. Meanwhile, a paper had been found nailed to the door of holywood abbey, the church. It was a poem of warning to four men. The first was Nick Appleyard who had already been killed. The second was Bennet Hatch. The third was Oliver Oates a priest and close friend of sir daniel brackley. Lastly the poem named Sir Brackley himself. The poem spoke of four black arrows that would pierce the four black hearts of these men. The poem also blamed these men for the death of sir Harry Shelton Richards father. Richard was naturally curious he determined to find out who was responsible for killing his father.

It was decided that richard would lead the new recruits to join Brackley. They arrived in kettley later that night. Brackley sent Richard back to tunstall with a message for Bennet Hatch. Richard was disappointed that he would not be fighting in the battle but he obeyed his guardian.

Quotes

A quote is the exact words of a speaker.

If someone says something directly, it is a **quote**.   Elise said, "I run a lot."

If someone else tells us what they said, it's not a quote.   Elise said she runs a lot.

Quotes are marked with **quotation marks**. They go around the speaker's words.

The first word of a quote is capitalized even if it is not the beginning of the sentence.

Elise explained, "Running is good exercise. I run every day."

If the quote is split, as shown in the example below, there are quotation marks at the

beginning and end of each part of the quote. Don't capitalize the beginning of the

second part of the quote unless it is the start of a new sentence.

"I can run for two miles," Elise commented, "without stopping."

Unless there is an exclamation point or question mark, use a comma to separate the

quote from the speaker's name. All punctuation goes inside the quotation marks.

"You should try running," Elise said.

Elise suggested, "We can run together."

"When would you like to start?" Elise asked.

Add capital letters and punctuation to the sentences below.

wow colin yelled did you see that

the doctor said make sure you rest   I will i replied

mom asked if we wanted some hot cocoa

i'm going to take a picture my brother said say cheese

41

Edit this passage from *The Black Arrow*.

About a mile from Kettley, richard heard someone call to him. A boy a little bit younger than himself stepped out from behind some weeds. He begged Richard to lead him to holywood abbey. Richard agreed to help him and he let the boy ride his horse while he walked alongside.

At Richard's prodding the boy introduced himself.

My name is John Matcham the boy said I am sixteen years old.

John explained that he was fleeing from Sir Brackley. Brackley had taken john by force. John had escaped and was desperate to reach the safety of Holywood. Richard vowed to lead John safely to the church the boys quickly became good friends.

John told Richard that sir brackley planned to marry Richard to a girl named Joanna Sedley for his own profit. John also spoke to Richard about Sir Brackley's role in the death of Richards father. John didn't understand why Richard defended Sir Brackley. Richard replied that he didnt know the facts, and until he did he would remain loyal to the man who had raised him.

Edit this passage from *The Black Arrow*.

As the two boys continued through the woods they spied a man keeping watch in a tree. They chose a different path but they heard another man singing. Spying some ruins, they hid themselves well. The man came around the corner, and soon he was joined by a large band of men. (They / Them) were the men of the black arrow, and they were talking about their plans to kill Sir Daniel. A signal sounded the men ran to their various stations.

john and richard came out of their hiding place. Richard wanted to warn sir daniel and his men but John did not. He pleaded with Richard to continue on to Holywood. Despite Johns pleading, Richard set off to warn his friends. He was too late to help them, and he was seen by one of the men of the black arrow. The boys again runned into the woods to hide.

Sir Brackley had disguised himself as a blind leper to escape from the men of the black arrow. He found the boys and took them to tunstall.

Edit this passage from *The Black Arrow*.

Once in Tunstall Richard was separated from john. He was curious what became of the boy, but he was more curious about who had killed his father. When Sir Brackley heard about richard's doubts he called his ward in for a talk. Richard asked his guardian if he had any part in the death of Sir Shelton but Sir Brackley denied it. He said that he was hurt by Richard's suspicions. Still Richard believed the knight was lying.

That night John snuck into Richard's room. He warned Richard that he had heard some men making plans to kill Richard! Just then the boys heard a loud cry followed by shouts for Joanna.

John crumbled. I am lost he cried. We must flee

Richard was confused. It took him only a moment to understand.

You're Joanna he asked. He stood for a moment and then spoke again.

Joanna we have both saved the other's life he said and if I live, I will indeed marry you gladly!

Midterm

Edit this passage from *The Black Arrow*.

richard and joanna slipped down a secret passageway. They entered a room where a long rope hanged out the window. At that moment several men barged into the room. They had been found Joanna fainted but Richard managed to escape out of the window. He swam across the moat and ran to safety. He knew that sir daniel would not harm Joanna, for he would profit richly from her marriage. Richard vowed to rescue her as soon as possible.

Richard was found by some men of the black arrow. They took (him / them) to their leader Ellis Duckworth.

Dont worry dear boy Ellis reassured him. You are now in the hands of someone who loved your father. I have vowed to avenge his death.

Richard had escaped from his deceitful guardian and was now among true friends. The men of the black arrow had been friends of his father. Richard joined them and becomed a respected leader.

Adjectives

Adjectives are words that describe nouns and pronouns.

Adjectives describe nouns and pronouns. **Possessives** function as adjectives.

<u>Megan's</u> horse has <u>long</u> <u>brown</u> mane and a <u>white</u> patch on <u>her</u> nose.

Adjectives are used to compare nouns and pronouns.

This is a <u>small</u> puppy, but there is a <u>smaller</u> puppy over there.

Proper adjectives are formed from proper nouns and are capitalized.

We've driven our <u>Ford</u> truck on many <u>Colorado</u> highways.

Predicate adjectives come after a linking verb.   That baby sounds <u>unhappy</u>.

Articles "a," "an," and "the" are adjectives.   <u>A</u> bird laid <u>an</u> egg in <u>the</u> nest.

Demonstrative adjectives are like demonstrative pronouns, but they are adjectives when they <u>do</u> name the noun.   <u>This</u> hat is for <u>that</u> snowman.

Indefinite adjectives are like indefinite pronouns, but they are adjectives when they <u>do</u> name the noun.   <u>Few</u> moths resist <u>all</u> lights.

Circle all of the adjectives in the sentences below.

Many tourists go to Florida towns to enjoy the warm weather.

Stephanie's bowling team got a better score than that team.

We went to a popular Mexican restaurant; the food was delicious.

Those three boys aren't wearing any shoes.

Read this passage from *The Black Arrow*. Circle as many adjectives as you can find.

Many months passed. The long war between the Lancaster and York houses continued. Sir Brackley fought for the Lancaster side, while Richard had joined the York party. Joanna was still in Sir Brackley's care, and Richard thought about her often. One day Richard learned that his lovely Joanna was to be married to Lord Shoreby.

Richard set off for the large town of Shoreby to find Joanna. Early one morning he heard a loud trumpet followed by the distinct clash of swords. He ran towards the sound and came upon a lone man in a desperate fight against seven others. Richard immediately jumped into the fight. After several moments of intense fighting, a band of men appeared and the fierce attackers ran away.

Richard had come to the aid of the Duke of Gloucester, an important leader of the York party.

Edit this passage from *The Black Arrow*.

The Duke of Gloucester was very grateful to richard. His band of men had responded to his trumpet call too late to help him. If Richard hadnt come to his rescue he would have been killed.

The duke of gloucester was leading his men to shoreby, where they would fight against the lancaster forces. The duke made Richard a commander and they devised a plan of attack. They would first seize a portion of the city, where they would set up their defense. They needed to hold the Lancaster forces back until more york reinforcements arrived.

After taking a quarter of the city by surprise and force Richard and the men under his command were assigned a street to defend. It didn't take long for the Lancaster forces to prepare themselves, and then the battle began in earnest. Richard and his men fought valiantly. Just as richard felt sure (they / them) could last no longer, the York reinforcements arrived. The Lancaster party scattered and the battle was winned.

Edit this passage from *The Black Arrow*.

The duke was extremely pleased with Richards bravery and leadership. He knighted Richard, dubbing him Sir Richard. Afterwards, Richard went to the house where Sir Brackley had been keeping Joanna. The house was a mess! It had been completely ransacked men were swarming into it and carrying out anything of value. Richard ran inside but neither Sir Brackley nor joanna (was / were) anywhere to be seen. Finding an archer who had been there when the house was taken, Richard learned that sir brackley had fled with twenty or so others. Whether Joanna had been among them the archer knowed not.

Richard returned to the Duke of Gloucester. He asked for some men to take in pursuit of Sir Brackley. The duke agreed and Richard set off with fifty men. They followed the trail left by Sir Brackley and his companions. Late in the evening Richard and his men comed upon the campfire of Sir Brackley. Richard realized too late that Sir Brackleys men had scattered and now surrounded them!

Edit this passage from *The Black Arrow*.

Richard's men immediately began to retreat. In the midst of the confusion, Joanna jumped off of her horse and runned to Richard's side. Seeing that they had only one chance of survival Richard and Joanna fled into the forest.

They came to holywood abbey in Tunstall just a few hours later As he had promised so long ago Richard brought Joanna safely to the church. They agreed to wed the very next day.

Early in the morning Richard went out for a walk. Just before (he / him) turned back to the church, he saw a lone man. It was Sir Brackley, defeated and forlorn. Richard decided to let Sir Brackley live but a black arrow whistled through the air and killed him. It was the arrow of Ellis Duckworth, who had finally taken his revenge for the death of sir shelton.

Richard and Joanna were married that same day. They became the new lord and lady of tunstall and they stayed in the great moathouse. There they lived in happiness, free from the miserys of war.

Adverbs

Adverbs are words that describe verbs, adjectives, and other adverbs.

Adverbs are similar to adjectives. However, adjectives describe nouns and pronouns, and adverbs describe verbs, adjectives, and other adverbs. Many adverbs end in **"-ly."**

Anne does <u>not</u> bake <u>daily</u>.   (Adverbs "not" and "daily" describing verbs)

She bakes <u>very</u> good bread.   (Adverb "very" describing adjective "good")

Anne bakes <u>really</u> <u>well</u>.   (Adverb "really" describing adverb "well")

Adverbs describe four basic things - **time**, **place**, **manner**, and **degree**.

Anne baked <u>yesterday</u>. (time)   Anne baked <u>here</u>. (place)

Anne bakes <u>happily</u>. (manner)   Anne bakes <u>constantly</u>. (degree)

Adverbs are also used to compare. For **comparative adverbs**, add **"-er"** to most one-syllable adverbs and use **more / less** before most two-or-more-syllable adverbs. For **superlative adverbs**, add **"-est"** to most one-syllable adverbs and use **most / least** before most two-or-more-syllable adverbs. **Irregular adverbs** change form completely.

He spoke <u>gently</u>. Lacy spoke <u>more</u> <u>gently</u> than he did.

My sisters sigh <u>dramatically</u>. I sigh <u>least</u> <u>dramatically</u> of all.

That clown juggles <u>badly</u>, but the clown over there juggles <u>worse</u>.

Complete the sentences below by writing adverbs in the blanks.

He laughs _____.   You swim _____.

This was _____ written.   She _____ travels.

That dog snarled ferociously. This one growled _____.

I know she sings well, but does she sing _____ than you?

Read this passage from *The Scarlet Pimpernel*. Circle as many adverbs as you can find.

The city of Paris was in turmoil in September of 1792. The French Revolution had quickly turned the streets of Paris into an endless scene of death. The common people had tired of living in poverty and oppression, and they had finally overthrown the rich nobles and aristocrats who ruled over France. Now the peasants ruthlessly sentenced dozens of aristocrats to death daily. The commoners watched the executions.

Another favorite sport of the common people was to go to the barricades, for aristocrats tried to escape fairly often. On this day there were many women leaving the city. They pushed carts for selling their goods at the market nearby. The guards carefully checked each cart. As one of the guards approached the cart of an ugly old woman, she cackled loudly and casually mentioned that her grandson had smallpox. The guard quickly backed away, yelling angrily at the ugly old woman.

The old woman was a man in disguise. He was using the cart to cleverly rescue three aristocrats from France.

Edit this passage from *The Scarlet Pimpernel*.

The three aristocrats and the man who had saved them made it safely to an inn in England, where (they / them) were free. The man belonged to a small group of men who risked their lifes to rescue the nobles of france. The leader of this group was known only as the Scarlet Pimpernel. His real identity was a mystery.

Two other guests happened to be staying at that very same inn. They were sir percy blakeney and his wife lady marguerite blakeney. Sir Percy was one of the richest men in England, and he was quite tall and very strong. He would have been called handsome if not for the dull lazy expression always on his face. He was known for his inane chatter and quick constant laugh.

His wife on the other hand was both very beautiful and exceedingly smart. She was from France, and everyone was surprised when she married such a dull man. Lady Blakeney grew tired of her husband's meaningless chatter and laugh but his devotion could not be faulted

Edit this passage from *The Scarlet Pimpernel.*

One fine autumn evening the blakeneys attended a ball in London. It was hosted by lord grenville. Sir Percy and Lady Marguerite Blakeney were quite respected by english society. They were very rich and always impeccably dressed in the latest fashions

Although Lady Blakeney usually enjoyed social functions she knew that she would not have a good time on this particular night. One of her old acquaintances from france a man by the name of Chauvelin was also at the ball. He was trying to catch the Scarlet Pimpernel. Chauvelin had forced Lady Blakeney into helping him. Her brother had been discovered to be part of the League of the Scarlet Pimpernel and Chauvelin had promised that he would go free if Lady Blakeney helped to gather information. Marguerite had been torn between her respect for the brave man who was rescuing so many of her countrymen and her love for her only brother.

In the end Marguerite knowed that she could not sentence her brother to death. She saw a note from the scarlet pimpernel and passed the information on to Chauvelin.

Edit this passage from *The Scarlet Pimpernel*.

Lady Blakeney feeled guilty. She was desperate to talk with someone so she decided to open up to her husband. However, as soon as she saw Percy with his lazy grin and annoying laugh, she knew he would be of no help. Sighing she climbed up beside him on the coach for the trip home.

Although sir percy had loved Lady Marguerite deeply at one time, something had changed after they'd gotten married. He had found out about something in Marguerites past. Before they'd been married, she had spoken harshly against a fellow frenchman. In the current, uncertain times, her words had been used at a trial. The aristocrat and his entire family were sentenced to death. Marguerite had been horrified but it didnt change her role in their deaths. It was true that Sir Percy lavished his riches upon lady marguerite and was a devoted husband, but the love was gone. Despite her indifference towards Percy for most of their relationship Lady Marguerite now realized how much she loved and missed (he / him).

Prepositions

Prepositions add meaning to sentences by showing time, location, direction, or how two things are related to one another.

Prepositions begin **prepositional phrases**. This phrase includes all of the words from the preposition up to a noun(s) or pronoun(s), which is the **object of the preposition**. The preposition shows how the object relates to another word in the sentence.

The toddler crawled <u>down the steps</u>.

A preposition is always followed by an object (a noun or pronoun). If there is no object, the word is most likely an adverb.   The toddler looked <u>down</u>.

Prepositional phrases can function as adjectives or adverbs. **Adjectival phrases** tell what kind or which one and modify nouns and pronouns. **Adverbial phrases** tell how, when, or where and modify verbs, adjectives, and adverbs.

The boys <u>with deep voices</u> stand <u>in the back row</u>.
            adjectival - what kind   adverbial - where

The airplane <u>with the blue tail</u> is departing <u>at noon</u>.
             adjectival - which one   adverbial - when

Underline the prepositional phrases. Identify them as adjectival or adverbial.

It rains often in the spring.   _____

Oranges from Florida are delicious.   _____

The man in the blue Illinois cap is my dad.   _____

He drank some water and then ran outside.   _____

I put the photos in an album.   _____

Read this passage from *The Scarlet Pimpernel*. Underline the prepositional phrases and circle the objects of the prepositions.

The next morning Lady Blakeney woke early after a short night of troubled sleep. She found a note from her husband; it said that he was leaving on unexpected business. He would be back within a week.

Marguerite got dressed and wandered around the house. She mused about her relationship with her husband and determined to fix things when he got back. As she passed his private study, she was overcome with curiosity. In all honesty, she had never before cared about the contents of this secretive room. Sir Percy usually kept the room locked, but today the door was open. Marguerite glanced around cautiously and entered.

The room was simply furnished. There were two maps of France on the wall, and a portrait of Sir Percy's mother hung by the desk. As Marguerite turned to leave, she accidentally sent a small object rolling across the floor. She picked it up and gasped. It was a solid gold ring, and it displayed the symbol of the Scarlet Pimpernel. Her husband was the mysterious hero!

Edit this passage from *The Scarlet Pimpernel*. Identify the underlined prepositional phrases as adjectival (adj.) or adverbial (adv.).

Lady Blakeney could hardly believe it yet she knew it was true. She realized all at once that sir percy's dull, lazy expression was simply a mask. Indeed she was sure no one would ever suspect that her husband was the courageous daring leader known as the scarlet pimpernel.

It didnt take Marguerite long to realize the danger she had unknowingly placed <u>upon her husband</u>. By giving the information to chauvelin and protecting her brother, she had betrayed her own husband! He had already left for france, and now she knew he was going to rescue more aristocrats. Chauvelin was probably following him. Once they were <u>in France</u>, the frenchman would arrest Sir Percy. Then Percy would be sentenced to death

Marguerite knew she had to warn her husband. She leaved at once for the home <u>of Sir Andrew Ffoulkes</u> her husband's good friend. She had correctly guessed that he was part of the League <u>of the Scarlet Pimpernel</u>, and she explained the situation to (he / him). They too left for France.

Edit this passage from *The Scarlet Pimpernel.*

Lady Marguerite and sir Andrew arrived at a certain inn in france. Sir Andrew told Marguerite that it was a common stop for the Scarlet Pimpernel and his men. Indeed, the innkeeper told them that a tall englishman had been there not long before. sir andrew went out to look for Sir Percy and Lady Marguerite stayed at the inn. She sitted in a room upstairs where (she / they) could watch the main room unnoticed.

The door opened. It was chauvelin He talked with the innkeeper and then sat down to eat. Lady Marguerite was trapped! She couldnt warn her husband without revealing herself to Chauvelin. all she could do was sit and hope that Sir Percy would not return to the inn.

One of Chauvelins men Desgas came in to report to Chauvelin. He told his master that the streets were all heavily guarded. The men were waiting they were watching for any tall stranger.

Edit this passage from *The Scarlet Pimpernel.*

Desgas returned with a dirty elderly jewish man a short while
later. The man had some information for Chauvelin. He and
another Jew had met a tall Englishman less than an hour before.
The Englishman had bought a horse and cart from them and then
had started towards a certain fishermans hut on the beach.

Chauvelin was thrilled at the news! He gathered as much
information as he could from the Jewish man. Then he ordered the
man to show him the way to the fisherman's hut. They left the inn
and disappeared into the night. lady blakeney had heard everything. She put on her cloak quietly slipped out of the inn and
followed the men. Keeping to the shadows she followed as closely
as possible without being seen.

A group of soldiers met Chauvelin and the jew on the road. They
had some news for Chauvelin they had found the fisherman's hut.
There were several men inside and they appeared to be waiting for
something.

Direct and Indirect Objects

Direct objects receive the action of the verb.

Indirect objects are the receivers of some direct objects.

A **direct object** is the noun or pronoun that directly receives the action of the verb.

To identify the direct object, ask *what* or *whom* received the action.

Jordan washed his <u>car</u>.

What did Jordan wash? His <u>car</u>.

I visited <u>her</u>.

Whom did I visit? <u>Her</u>.

Some sentences may have **compound** (more than one) direct objects.

She read the <u>newspaper</u> and a <u>magazine</u>.

Some sentences with direct objects also have **indirect objects**. An indirect object names the person (or thing) *to whom* or *for whom* something was done.

My mom ordered <u>me</u> a turkey sandwich.

What did Mom order? A <u>sandwich</u>. For whom was it ordered? <u>Me</u>.

There may also be compound indirect objects.

Justin handed <u>Levi</u> and <u>Keith</u> a heavy package.

What was handed? A <u>package</u>. To whom was it handed? <u>Levi</u> and <u>Keith</u>.

Identify any direct objects (DO) or indirect objects (IO) in the sentences below.

Caroline gave her dog a bath last week.

The child drew his dad a picture of a big red truck.

Will you tell me a story?

He opened and read the letter immediately.

Edit this passage from *The Scarlet Pimpernel*. Identify any direct or indirect objects in the underlined sentences.

Chauvelin understood exactly what was happening. The men in the hut were aristocrats and they were waiting for the Scarlet Pimpernel to come for them. <u>Chauvelin gave his men very strict orders.</u> They were to keep watch around the fisherman's hut, but no one was to move in until the tall englishman was seen. Chauvelin threatened to kill any soldier who made a move before the scarlet pimpernel arrived.

It wasnt very long until the group was within sight of the hut. Knowing that her husband was in grave danger Marguerite made a run for the hut. she was desperate to warn the men inside for they could then escape and warn Sir Percy. Marguerite slipped and fell down. <u>Chauvelin heard the noise.</u> He sended one of his soldiers after her. Before she could reach the hut marguerite was caught. <u>The soldier took her to Chauvelin.</u> He told her that one of the men in the hut was her brother. If she cooperated her brother would be set free. If she didn't, all of the men in the hut would be killed.

Edit this passage from *The Scarlet Pimpernel.*

Chauvelin was determined to catch the Scarlet Pimpernel, and he would not allow lady blakeney to destroy his plans. Knowing Marguerite would not risk her brothers life, he left her alone. He had the jewish man bound and gagged to ensure that he wouldn't make any noise.

Marguerite felt absolutely helpless. She dreaded the arrival of her husband the Scarlet Pimpernel. His death seemed unstoppable!

Suddenly they heard a man singing. Recognizing her husband's voice Marguerite cried out a warning. She was thrown roughly to the ground and silenced. The singing stopped. Chauvelin ordered his men to storm the hut and kill everyone inside. The soldiers charged into the hut but no shots were fired. There was no one inside The soldiers explained that they had seen the men slip out of the hut some time before. Because chauvelin had ordered them to wait until the tall Englishman arrived, they hadn't attacked (they / them). Chauvelin was outraged, but it was true. He had told the men they would be killed if they moved before the Scarlet Pimpernel arrived they had obeyed.

63

Edit this passage from *The Scarlet Pimpernel*.

Chauvelin and the soldiers quickly moved out to search the beach for the singer and the escaped aristocrats. Marguerite was left alone with the Jew. She wondered if her husband and brother were safely out of france.

As the soldiers disappeared from sight Marguerite heard her husband's voice! Confused she looked around. He spoke again, and Marguerite whirled to face the jewish man. It was Sir Percy His clever disguise had fooled Chauvelin and his own wife! After hearing chauvelins strict orders, percy had freed himself from his bindings. Then he had crept up to the hut and slipped a note inside. The note instructed the men to go down the beach to where a boat was hidden. Percy had waited a while and then started singing loudly. No one had suspected the old jew, and the men had escaped to safety. Sir Percy had also told them to send a boat back for lady Blakeney and (himself / themselves), and it was on its way. Marguerite falled into her husband's arms. Gazing into his eyes Marguerite saw that they were filled with love.

The daring scarlet pimpernel had succeeded once again

Edit this passage from *The Time Machine*.

i sat with a handful of other men at a friends table. He had invited us to supper this fine thursday evening in order to share his latest experiment with us. He warned us that what he was about to say contradicted some of the principles we had been taught in school. When he finished his explanation we sat shocked. He claimed to have invented a machine that could travel through time

Our friend we'll call him the Time Traveller disappeared into his lab and returned with a small model. It had a seat levers knobs and many other tiny parts. the Time Traveller told us that it was a working model of his time machine. He asked one of the men to push one of the little levers, and the machine began to quiver. Then it disappeared The Time Traveller insisted that it had traveled into the future. We didnt believe that it had really traveled through time but there was no other explanation.

Confusing Words

Some words are often confused with similar words.

Here are some tips to help you remember which word to use when:

good - good is an adjective

This is a <u>good</u> swim team.

well - well is an adverb

The children swim very <u>well</u>.

than - used to make comparisons

I used to be taller <u>than</u> my sister.

then - tells when

<u>Then</u> she grew four more inches.

affect - a verb meaning "to influence"

Does this news <u>affect</u> you?

effect - a noun meaning "result"

Actually, it has no <u>effect</u> on me.

among   - used with more than two

I saw a flower <u>among</u> the weeds.

between - used with only two

I saw an alley <u>between</u> the stores.

imply - to suggest (speaker)

The man <u>implied</u> he had an idea.

infer - to draw a conclusion (listener)

I <u>inferred</u> that it was a good one.

farther - a physical distance

He lives <u>farther</u> away than I do.

further - time, quantity, or degree

<u>Further</u> details will be provided.

Circle the correct words in the sentences below.

I live in a (good / well) neighborhood. It's (among / between) two parks.

The article (implied / inferred) that girls read more (than / then) boys.

The case required (farther / further) investigation.

The caffeine had an (affect / effect) for a while, but (than / then) I slept.

Edit this passage from *The Time Machine*.

I went back to the Time Travellers house one week later. Several men (was / were) sitting at the supper table. I sat down (among / between) them. Only one of the men had been there the previous week. The Time Traveller was not at the table. We began to talk about where he might be.

The door opened. In limped the Time Traveller. He was covered with dust and dirt and he looked pale and exhausted. He motioned for something to drink. One of the men handed him a glass of water. The Time Traveller gulped it down and (than / then) filled his plate with food. He told us that he had a (good / well) story to tell, but he had to satisfy his immense hunger first. We watched him curiously.

Just one question i begged. have you been time traveling

I have he answered. His serious response did not (imply / infer) that he was joking.

The Time Traveller began to eat while the rest of us exchanged doubtful questioning glances. We didn't question him (farther / further). When he had finished eating we retired to a comfortabler room. Then he began his story.

Edit this passage from *The Time Machine*.

He had finished the time machine that very morning. He climbed onto the seat pulled the starting lever and then quickly pulled the stopping lever. In just that short amount of time, he noted from the clock that several hours had passed. The Time Traveller pulled the starting lever again. the machine started to whirl and shake as time slipped by faster and faster. He watched his surroundings change as the years flew by. When he finally pulled the stopping lever he was throwed from the machine. Disoriented he stood up and looked around. He was in a grassy field. A large statue loomed nearby. There (was / were) a handful of gigantic buildings (farther / further) off in the distance. It was very warm outside and everything looked calm and peaceful. checking one of the dials on the time machine, the Time Traveller noted that it was the year 802701. (Than / Then) he taked the levers off the machine and put them in his pocket for safekeeping. As he continued to scan the landscape, he saw several persons approaching (he / him).

Edit this passage from *The Time Machine*.

The Time Traveller was struck by their strange appearance. The people were about four feet tall and were clothed in colorful robes They (was / were) very beautiful but also very frail. The thing that surprised the Time Traveller the most was that they showed no signs of fear. Instead they laughed when they saw him and chattered loudly to one another. He could not understand their language but they seemed very friendly.

The Time Traveller followed the little people into one of the big buildings. It was beautifully constructed but obviously very old and worn. There were tables filled with all kinds of strange fruit. The little people sitted down on cushions and began to eat. the time traveller joined them and he began to try and learn their language. Although this amused the people for a while they soon became bored and simply ignored him. He did however manage to learn that they were called Eloi.

The Time Traveller was disappointed. He had expected the people of the future to be brilliant. Instead, the eloi seemed more like childs.

Edit this passage from *The Time Machine*.

After the Time Traveller finished eating he went back outside to explore. As (he / him) thought about these people of the future he realized what had happened. Man had become so accustomed to adapting the world to his needs that there was no longer anything to worry about or fear. without the need for strength, the (affect / effect) was that man had become weak. The Eloi simply led such comfortable lifes that they had no reason to be anything but happy thoughtless children.

After reaching this conclusion, the Time Traveller returned to the field where he had first arrived. The time machine was gone Frantic, he searched for any sign of the machine. He had taken the levers off so he knew it had only been moved. There were tracks in the grass leading to the giant statue Rapping on the panels in the base, the Time Traveller realized that it was hollow. It was easy to figure out that the time machine had been put inside of the statue but who had done it He tried to open the panels they wouldnt budge.

Modifiers

Modifiers provide additional information about the words they modify.

Modifiers have to be placed correctly for clear meaning. If a modifier is modifying the wrong word or it is unclear which word in the sentence it is modifying, it is called a **misplaced modifier**. A modifier is a **dangling modifier** if its subject isn't included in the sentence at all or when its intended subject isn't the actual subject of the sentence.

Here is an example of a misplaced modifier. The sentence is very confusing.

My sister took out the garbage <u>with a frown</u>.   The garbage was frowning?

<u>With a frown</u>, my sister took out the garbage.   This sentence is clear.

Here is an example of a dangling modifier. The subject is not what was intended.

<u>Sitting by the lake</u>, the duck splashed me.   Subject seems to be "duck."

<u>Sitting by the lake</u>, I was splashed by a duck.   Correct. "I" is now the subject.

Rewrite the sentences below so that the meanings are clear.

There is a restaurant next to the gas station that serves wonderful food.

After singing many Christmas carols, my eyes were droopy.

Watching through the window, the birds gathered at the feeder.

She told her daughter to lift the glass vase with two hands.

Driving home from the store, the baby remained asleep.

Edit this passage from *The Time Machine*. Find and underline one misplaced modifier and one dangling modifier.

It didnt take very long for the Time Traveller to realize that there was something the Eloi feared. They were terrified of the dark. As soon as the sun set they all went inside for the night. They slept in large groups in the buildings all huddled together.

The Time Traveller waked up early one morning. It was still dark outside. Feeling restless, he went outside to watch the sun rise. in the first rays of light, (he / him) saw several human-like creatures scurrying across the ground. He tried to follow one. It did have some characteristics of a person but it was not beautiful like the eloi. It was very pale had large gray eyes and light hair and moved with surprising speed and agility. It entered what looked like a well and disappeared from view. Peering down the shaft, the darkness had already hidden the small creature. Only his large eyes (was / were) visible in the oppressive blackness.

Edit this passage from *The Time Machine*.

The Time Traveller was puzzled about the pale creatures. He learned from the Eloi that they were called Morlocks. The eloi spoke of them with shivers and fearful glances and they refused to go near any of the openings to the underground. The Time Traveller realized that the Morlocks lived underground and comed out only at night.

It didnt take very long for the time traveller to reach a new conclusion. The Eloi were the descendants of the richer class of people. They now enjoyed a comfortable lifestyle and had no memory of work. They had become weak mindless people. The morlocks (was / were) the descendants of the common laborers They had been the people who toiled away in large mines and underground railways. As time went by they had spent more and more time working in underground factorys. Over time they had become so accustomed to the dark that they could no longer live in the light. they had become strong people who worked and ruled the dark.

Edit this passage from *The Time Machine*.

The Time Traveller felt sure that the Morlocks had put the time machine in the base of the statue. When he questioned the eloi about the statue they ran away in disgust. The Time Traveller had no choice. If he wanted to find his way back home he had to go into the underground world of the morlocks.

Two days passed before he worked up the courage to climb down into the shaft. The Time Traveller gathered his strength and started down the dark passage. He could hear deep voices and the hum of machinery. when he got to the bottom, he felt the Morlocks pressing in around him. He lit a match and they ran away from the light. As soon as the match burned out, they crept up to him again. The dark heavy atmosphere seemed to close in around him. The Morlocks grabbed at his clothing. He lit another match they fled for a second time. Realizing he was out of matches the Time Traveller turned to leave. He climbed out of reach just before the morlocks could drag him (farther / further) into their underground world.

Edit this passage from *The Time Machine*.

The time travellers only hope was to break into the base of the statue. He explored more of the eloi's world in search of something he could use to pry open the panels. After finding an iron crowbar, he returned to the statue. Surprisingly the panels were open. The Time Traveller saw his time machine sitting inside. The Morlocks were trying to trap him

Fingering the levers in his pocket, the Time Traveller stepped inside the statue As he approached the time machine the panels slid shut behind him. he could hear the evil giggles of the Morlocks as they creeped towards him. The Time Traveller worked in the dark as quickly as he could to refasten the levers to the time machine. He climbed on to the machine as the Morlocks surrounded him. (They / Them) grabbed and pulled at his clothes, and he fought with all of his strength to stay on the machine. He pulled the starting lever The machine whirred to life and he feeled the Morlocks hands fall away.

Labeling Sentences

There are many different parts of speech, including subjects, verbs, adjectives, adverbs, prepositions and prepositional phrases, and direct and indirect objects. Here is a quick review:

The subject is who or what the sentence is about.

The verb tells the action of the subject or provides more information. There are action, linking, and helping verbs.

Adjectives modify nouns and pronouns.

Adverbs modify verbs, adjectives, and other adverbs.

Prepositions begin prepositional phrases, which end with a noun or pronoun.

The direct object receives the action of the verb.
The indirect object is the receiver of the direct object.

In the sentences below, underline the subjects once and the verbs twice. Circle the adjectives. Mark the adverbs (ADV), the direct objects (DO), and the indirect objects (IO). Cross out any prepositional phrases.

I secretly bought my older sister a new necklace for her birthday.

Inside the pen, the five little pigs wallowed in the mud.

Cadence is happily playing with her toys on the floor.

Jordan scored two points during the first half of the basketball game.

Edit this passage from *The Time Machine*.

The time traveller set the dials on the machine to return home. He traveled back into the past at an incredible speed. He watched time pass in reverse until (he / him) recognized the world once again. He slowed his speed and eventually he saw the familiar sight of his own laboratory. He carefully pulled the stopping lever When he climbed off, he heard our voices in the dining room. Feeling exhausted and weak he joined us for supper.

That was the end of the Time Traveller's story. It was a fantastic tale but we could hardly accept it as truth! We didnt know what to think.

I returned to the Time Travellers house the very next day to ask more questions. Just as I opened the door to his laboratory, i heard a sound like a strong sharp wind. I seemed to see just a trace of the Time Traveller on his time machine before it vanished. I have been waiting for years and the Time Traveller has yet to return.

Edit this passage from *Great Expectations*.

When Pip, whose christian name was Philip, was just seven years old, something happened that changed his life forever. He was visiting the graves of his parents and brothers when a dirty rough man grabbed him by the shoulders. The man had an iron shackle on one of his legs. He was an escaped prisoner and he ordered Pip to come back the next day with some food and a file. Pip was terrified of the man and his threats! He agreed and ran home as quickly as he could.

Pip lived by the marshs with his sister mrs. Joe Gargery and her husband Mr. Joe Gargery. Joe was a blacksmith and was not well-educated but he was always kind to Pip. Mrs. Joe on the other hand constantly complained about having the additional burden of Pip. She ruled the household and was quick to punish pip for any fault, no matter how slight.

The next day Pip stole some food out of the pantry took a file from joes shop and ran through the marshes to meet the prisoner. After giving him the items, Pip went home. He knew he'd be in trouble when Mrs Joe discovered the missing food.

Edit this passage from *Great Expectations*.

Pip waited nervously for mrs joe to realize that some of the food was gone. It was christmas, and they had company over. Just as she discovered a missing pie there was a knock on the door. It was a group of soldiers! Pip thought they had come for him, but the sergeant was looking for Joe. He needed a pair of handcuffs fixed for they were going after the escaped prisoner.

after mending the handcuffs, joe and pip went with the soldiers to find the prisoner. As they got closer and closer to the marshes, they heard two mans yelling. Following the noise they came upon two prisoners. They (was / were) fighting. The prisoner Pip had met explained that he was determined not to let the other prisoner escape. Even though it prevented him from escaping, he wanted to make sure the soldiers caught the other prisoner. He didnt say anything to Pip he told the soldiers he'd stolen food from the blacksmiths house. Joe was stunned and Pip was relieved.

Edit this passage from *Great Expectations*.

One day Mrs Joe came home with some surprising news. Pip was to go to Miss Havisham's house the very next day. Miss Havisham was a rich mysterious lady who lived in a large house. Pip was not looking forward to the trip but mrs. joe was thrilled. She thought that if Pip pleased the old woman, Miss Havisham would give them some money.

When Pip arrived at Miss Havishams house, a pretty girl named Estella opened the door. She led him to miss Havisham's room. Pip entered and looked around. Miss Havisham was a pale, old woman. She hadnt been outside for many years, and she wore a wedding gown that was yellow with age. An old mouse-eaten wedding cake sat on a table Everything in the room (was / were) covered in cobwebs. The clocks were all stopped at the same time. Miss Havisham wanted Pip to entertain her. He didn't quite know what to do so she ordered him to play cards with estella.

Pip went back to Miss Havisham's house many times to keep the old woman company. Estella always treated him badly but Pip admired (she / her) anyway.

Diagramming Sentences

Sentence diagrams show how the words relate to each other.

A **sentence diagram** is a visual picture of a sentence. The subject and verb go on the main line separated by a vertical line. Predicate nouns or adjectives (those which come after a linking verb) go after the verb, separated by a diagonal line.

| Eve | is driving |

| She | was \ unhappy |

Adjectives and adverbs go on slanted lines beneath the words they modify. Direct objects go on the main line after the verb, separated by a vertical line. Indirect objects belong on a horizontal line beneath the verb, connected by a diagonal line.

Prepositional phrases also go beneath the words they modify. The preposition goes on a slanted line, which leads to the object of the preposition on a new horizontal line.

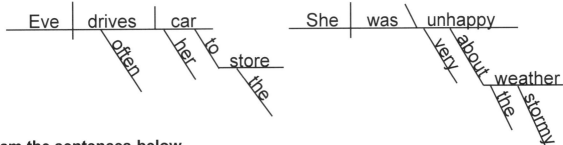

Diagram the sentences below.

My best friend often wears her blue sweater.

Those kids are playing football in the mud.

A noisy bird is chirping loudly outside my bedroom window.

The doctor wrote him a prescription on yellow paper.

She slowly handed me the crossword puzzle from the newspaper.

81

Edit this passage from *Great Expectations*.

a year or so later Pip was old enough to be apprenticed to joe. Miss Havisham gave Joe some money for pip's services and told Pip he no longer needed to come and visit her. Although Pip had dreamed of the day he would start his apprenticeship he was no longer excited. Estella had made Pip realize that he was common he was now ashamed of the simple trade. Every day he worried that estella would see him working and covered with soot.

Pip now went to see miss havisham just once a year. Estella had gone abroad to study, and Miss Havisham took an odd sort of delight in the fact that Pip missed her. Pip worked for Joe for many years and he thought of Estella more as time passed. He was determined to become a gentleman in order to gain Estellas love. Pip shared his feelings with Biddy the girl who helped Mrs. Joe around the house. Biddy, who was kind and sensible, told Pip he shouldn't have to change in order to win love. Pip wished he could love biddy instead but his heart had been captured by Estella.

Edit this passage from *Great Expectations*.

One saturday night a man approached Joe and Pip. Pip
recognized the man as someone he'd seen many years ago at Miss
Havisham's house. The man introduced himself as mr. jaggers.
He was a lawyer and had brought news for Pip. An anonymous
benefactor had taken an interest in pip. The common boy had
come into a great fortune and was to be educated as a gentleman!
There were two conditions. Pip (was / were) to keep the name of
Pip and the benefactor was to remain a mystery until he or she
decided to reveal his or her identity. Mr Jaggers also offered Joe
some money for he would be losing Pip's help. Joe refused.

Pips dreams had come true He was going to be a gentleman!
Mr. Jaggers told him that he would leave for london at once to start
his education. Matthew Pocket one of Miss Havisham's relatives
was going to be his tutor. Even though his benefactor wished to
remain a mystery, Pip (implied / inferred) that it was miss
havisham.

Edit this passage from *Great Expectations*.

Within a few days pip became somewhat arrogant. He was ashamed of Joe's simple uneducated ways and was eager to begin his life as a gentleman in London.

Once in london Pip finded his way to the office of Mr. Jaggers. The lawyer explained that Pip could get money from him and that Pip had credit all over town to buy whatever he needed. Pip would be staying at the inn with matthew pocket's son for a few days before going to Matthew's house.

The sons name was herbert. Pip had seen him once at Miss Havisham's many years ago when they were both young boys. Herbert and Pip became great friends and Herbert told Pip every-thing he knew about his mysterious relative. Miss Havisham had been swindled by a man who had pretended to love her. She had loved him deeply and had gived him a lot of money. On the day of their wedding he had never come. She had weared her wedding dress and stayed inside ever since. Miss Havisham had adopted Estella and raised (she / her) to break men's hearts.

Edit this passage from *Great Expectations*.

Pip settled into his new lifestyle. He spent some of his time with matthew pocket being educated but he continued to live with Herbert at the inn. While pip had money to spend Herbert did not. Both boys spended much more (than / then) they could afford and ran up steep debts.

Mrs. Joe died some time later; Pip went home for her funeral. Not long afterwards Pip turned twenty-one He expected to find out the name of his benefactor but Mr. Jaggers merely handed him an envelope filled with money. From now on Pip would receive a set amount of money each year and mr Jaggers would no longer be involved. Pip used the money to secretly secure a (good / well) job for herbert.

A couple of weeks after Pip turned twenty-three, there was a knock on the door. being alone in the house, pip answered the door. It was the prisoner from his childhood The man entered the house and began talking. Pip was horrified. (Than / Then) the man said that he was Pips benefactor!

Sentence Combining

Sometimes it is helpful to combine two or more short sentences into one longer sentence.

Instead of using several short, choppy sentences, sometimes two or more thoughts can be combined into one sentence.

My grandma knit a scarf for me. It was blue. She also made a scarf for my sister. My sister's scarf was red.

These four sentences can easily be combined into a single sentence.

My grandma knit a blue scarf for me and a red scarf for my sister.

Combine each group of sentences below into one sentence.

I like chili. It is my favorite meal. It is perfect on a cold day.

He read three books. They were big books. The books were about wars. It took him two weeks.

The farmer planted corn. He also planted beans. He planted an acre of each. The farmer planted them two months ago.

The baby had big blue eyes. She also had blonde hair. The baby was smiling. She had three little teeth.

I share a bedroom with my sister. She is older than me. Her name is Bethany.

Edit this passage from *Great Expectations*.

The man's name was Magwitch and he told his story to Pip. He had been in and out of jail for most of his life. He had never forgotten Pips kindness in bringing him food years ago. After serving that particular sentence Magwitch had decided that he would work hard and give all of his money to pip. He knew that he could never be more than a common fellow but he took pride in knowing that he was making a gentleman.

Pip did not feel the least bit grateful. He had thought he was being aided by miss havisham, not some dirty criminal!

Through conversations with Magwitch Herbert Mr. Jaggers and Miss Havisham Pip was finally able to piece together the mystery surrounding Estella. Mr. Jaggers' housekeeper had been the wife of magwitch. She had committed a crime, and then she'd disappeared from Magwitch's life along with their young daughter. Mr. Jaggers had helped the woman stay out of jail and had sent her daughter to live with Miss Havisham. Magwitch was estella's father

Edit this passage from *Great Expectations*.

Pip and Herbert discovered another bit of news after hearing Magwitchs story. He had once worked for a man by the name of Compeyson the very same man who had swindled Miss Havisham! Magwitch and Compeyson had both been arrested but compeyson made sure the evidence fell more heavily upon Magwitch. Compeyson was also a very well-bred man, a fact which had helped him get a more short prison term than Magwitch. When Pip and the soldiers had found Magwitch long ago it was Compeyson whom Magwitch had been holding.

Although Magwitch was very pleased with his success in creating a gentleman, pip secretly decided that he would spend no more of the money.

Magwitch's life was in danger now that he had come back to london. He had been sent overseas and was not supposed to ever return. Knowing Magwitch would not leave him Pip and Herbert devised a plan to get both Magwitch and Pip out of London safely.

Meanwhile estella had married a brutish man out of boredom. She hadn't married for love for miss havisham had never shown her what love was.

Edit this passage from *Great Expectations*.

Pip was being watched he knew that Compeyson and the authorities were trying to find Magwitch. (He / Him) and herbert did their best to figure out a (good / well) way to get Pip's benefactor out of england. When the day came, Pip and Herbert picked up Magwitch by boat. he wore a long cloak and seemed content just to be in Pip's company. Just before reaching a steamer bound for germany a boat full of officers overtook them.

Compeyson was in the boat he had led the officers to Magwitch. Both magwitch and compeyson falled overboard in the confusion that followed. Only Magwitch came back to the surface. He had two broken ribs and a punctured lung from hitting the side of the boat but he was arrested anyway.

Magwitch wasnt upset about going back to prison He was happy just to have seen the gentleman he'd made out of pip. As for Pip, he gained respect for Magwitch and his deep generosity. He did not tell his benefactor that all of magwitchs money and property would now be seized by the state, leaving Pip poor once again.

Final Examination

Edit this passage from *Great Expectations*.

Magwitch was sentenced to death but his injurys were so serious that it was clear he wouldnt live to be executed. Pip stayed by his side and holded his hand as much as he could. magwitch died happy he had succeeded in making a gentleman and knew that his daughter was alive.

After magwitch's death Pip became quite ill. He was in so much debt that he was arrested, but Pip fainted at that very moment. When he woke up, Joe was taking care of him. Pip felt deeply ashamed for the way he'd treated Joe. one morning Pip awoke to find that joe had left. There was a note along with a receipt on the table. Joe had paid all of pips bills before returning home!

Pip went to work with herbert who was now a successful businessman. While Pip never became rich he did quite (good / well) and was very happy. Many years later he returned home to visit. joe and biddy (was / were) married and had two children one of whom was a son named Pip. estella was also back in town. Her husband had died some years ago. She told Pip that she hoped (they / them) could finally be friends

Complete Sentences

Identify run-ons or fragments. In the others, underline the complete subject once and complete predicate twice. Circle each simple subject and simple predicate.

My mom bought a new camera.

The window broke during the storm.

Typed a long letter. (fragment)

Jillian made a beautiful collage.

The unbearable drought lasted for three long months.

Our favorite dentist retired last week.

The coffee was good and I liked the donuts but the milk was too warm. (run-on)

1

Read this passage from *Uncle Tom's Cabin*. Identify any run-on sentences. Make sure each underlined sentence is complete. If it is, circle the simple subject and the simple predicate. If it is not, identify the fragment as a subject (s) or a predicate (p).

The Shelbys lived in an elegant house in Kentucky. Owned a number of slaves.(p) They prided themselves on treating them well. Mrs. Shelby, in particular, did her best to train them in the Christian faith and treat them as equals. It came as a great surprise when her husband announced that he had sold two of their slaves. She began to argue at once, but he told her it was no use. They were deeply in debt. Mr. Haley, a slave trader, was taking Tom and Harry in the morning.

Tom, affectionately known as Uncle Tom, was the Shelby's best hand. He was honest, hardworking, and trustworthy. Mr. Shelby was sorry to part with such a valuable slave. Harry was a young boy of only four years. Was a handsome, entertaining boy.(p)

Harry's mother, Eliza.(s) She overheard the Shelbys talking. Eliza quickly packed some provisions, picked up Harry, and left the house. Stopping by Tom's cabin, she told the other slaves the news. Eliza had decided to run away with her son she asked them to get word to her husband George who worked on a nearby farm. (run-on) Then she disappeared into the night.

2

Sentence Types

It is sometimes possible to end a sentence more than one way. The most common confusion is whether to use a period or an exclamation point. In certain instances either one can be used with only a slight change in meaning. For this reason, it is not "wrong" if students use periods in place of exclamation points or vice versa, unless the sentence obviously requires one or the other. If this ever happens, simply take the opportunity to discuss both possibilities and decide which would be more effective.

Add capital letters and ending punctuation to the sentences below. Identify the type of each one.

The blue paint matched the carpet perfectly. ___declarative___

We're going to be late! ___exclamatory___

Unlock the door. ___imperative___

Alicia wore her new coat. ___declarative___

Are you going on the ski trip this winter? ___interrogative___

Jump in the pond. ___imperative___

The tiger is loose! ___exclamatory___

3

Edit this passage from *Uncle Tom's Cabin* by adding capital letters and ending punctuation where needed. Use all three types of ending punctuation.

There are 11 errors in this passage.

Chloe, Tom's wife, urged Tom to try and escape as well. She asked him, "Why don't you go with Eliza and Harry?"

"I can't, Chloe," Tom replied. "If I don't go, someone else will have to take my place. I can bear it just as well as anyone else. Besides, Master has always been able to count on me. I won't break his trust now."

Mr. Haley arrived early the next morning. When he found out that Eliza had run away with Harry, he was outraged! He demanded help tracking them down. Mr. Shelby ordered two slaves to help him. Mrs. Shelby encouraged them to do what they could to slow the slave trader down.

After tracking Eliza for several hours, they found her waiting for a boat to cross the icy Ohio River. When she spotted the tracking party, Eliza ran towards the river. Mr. Haley saw her and gave a shout. Eliza called out to God, held Harry tight, and jumped onto a piece of ice! Falling and slipping, she continued bounding across the river on the floating pieces of ice. When she reached the other side, she swiftly climbed up the bank. They had escaped!

4

Review Time!

Edit this passage from *Uncle Tom's Cabin*. Underline any sentence fragments and identify them as subjects (s) or predicates (p).

There are 9 errors in this passage.

<u>Watched Eliza with a scowl.</u>(p) Mr. Haley didn't have time to wait for a boat to take him across the river. <u>H</u>e hired a pair of slave catchers to find Eliza and Harry, and then he returned to the Shelby's property for Tom.

Mrs. Shelby was in the cabin talking to Tom and Chloe when Mr. Haley arrived<u>.</u> She told Tom that she would do her best to buy him back again. Then Mr. Haley interrupted and growled at Tom that it was time to leave. <u>T</u>om obediently climbed up into the wagon, and Mr. Haley fastened a pair of shackles around his ankles. They slowly rolled away as those left behind wept.

<u>M</u>r. Haley was taking Tom to New Orleans by boat. He hoped to sell Tom for a lot of money. Mr. Haley was a very greedy man<u>!</u>

<u>A father and daughter by the name of St. Clare.</u>(s) They happened to be on the same boat. The daughter, Eva, was a charming girl of five years<u>.</u> Her generous, compassionate nature impressed everyone who met her. <u>H</u>er father was a wealthy, careless man whose life revolved around his only child.

5

Nouns

Sometimes words like "Mom" and "Dad" may take the place of a name. For example, in the sentence "<u>D</u>ad picked up the mail," *Dad* is capitalized because it is used in place of a name - "<u>T</u>imothy picked up the mail." However, in the sentence "<u>My dad</u> picked up the mail," it is not capitalized because you would not put a name there - "<u>My Timothy</u> picked up the mail."

Titles used with names are capitalized - "<u>U</u>ncle <u>T</u>imothy."

Identify the nouns in the first column as common or proper. Identify the nouns in the second column as concrete or abstract.

doctor	common	wind	concrete
Asia	proper	light	concrete
park	common	fear	abstract
Dr. Hamaker	proper	garden	concrete
Titanic	proper	impatience	abstract
Super Bowl	proper	honesty	abstract
airplane	common	Mars	concrete

6

Read this passage from *Uncle Tom's Cabin*. Circle at least fifteen common nouns. Underline and capitalize the proper nouns.

<u>Eva</u> made friends with everyone on the boat, and she took a special interest in <u>Tom</u>. She asked her father to buy <u>Tom</u>, and <u>Mr. St. Clare</u> agreed. When the boat arrived in <u>New Orleans</u>, <u>Tom</u> accompanied <u>Eva</u> and her father to their house. <u>Tom</u> was deeply impressed by the beautiful mansion and lavish furnishings. He was surprised to see the other slaves in rich clothing. It didn't take long for <u>Tom</u> to see that they were used to an easy lifestyle. Indeed, the slaves were just as lazy and wasteful as <u>Mr. St. Clare</u> himself, and they thought themselves better than other slaves.

The things required of <u>Tom</u> were not very difficult. He spent much of his time with <u>Eva</u>. She read his <u>Bible</u> out loud to him, and he sang songs to her. In time the honest character of <u>Tom</u> won the respect of <u>Mr. St. Clare</u>. <u>Tom</u> was made the manager of the expenses. He handled this responsibility much more wisely than any of those before him.

<u>Eva</u> helped <u>Tom</u> write a letter to his family. He wanted them to know that he had been bought by a kind master.

7

Capitalization

Point out to students that small, unimportant words like "the," "a," and "of" in titles are not usually capitalized unless they are the first word of the title.

Add capital letters and periods where they belong in the sentences below.

<u>W</u>e are going to a <u>C</u>hristmas party next <u>F</u>riday<u>.</u>
<u>M</u>y mother and <u>I</u> had supper at a <u>J</u>apanese restaurant<u>.</u>
<u>D</u>rew enjoyed playing soccer for <u>C</u>oach <u>J. A</u>nderson last year<u>.</u>
<u>P</u>lease show me the correct way to fold an <u>A</u>merican flag<u>.</u>
<u>T</u>his letter was supposed to be delivered to <u>M</u>rs<u>. H. L</u>ong<u>.</u>
<u>O</u>n <u>I</u>ndependence <u>D</u>ay <u>I</u> am going to see the fireworks<u>.</u>
<u>P</u>rof<u>. P</u>amela <u>C. B</u>riggs enjoys eating <u>D</u>anish pastries for breakfast<u>.</u>

8

Edit this passage from *Uncle Tom's Cabin*.

There are 17 errors in this passage.

Meanwhile, Eliza and Harry had been helped along by various people until they had reached the safety of a Quaker settlement. Eliza's husband, George, had met up with them there. His master was a cold, ruthless man, and George had managed to escape and join his family. Although they faced many dangerous circum-stances, the tired refugees finally made it to Canada and freedom. They didn't own a single thing, yet they were happier than they had ever been before. With the help of a kind missionary, they started a brand new life.

It had now been two years since that fateful February day when Tom was sold. Although he missed his family, those years had been pleasant for Tom. Eva St. Clare had only grown more attached to the faithful slave, and he was completely devoted to her. One day when they were sitting in the garden, Eva became very serious. She pointed to the clouds.

"I'm going soon, Tom," she stated. "I've seen angels, and I know I'm going to live with them soon."

9

Review Time!

Edit this passage from *Uncle Tom's Cabin*.

There are 20 errors in this passage.

It wasn't very long before everyone could see the truth in the words Eva had spoken. Her skin grew pale, and she lost weight. Some days she hardly had enough strength to stand. The months passed, and Eva grew weaker and weaker. Tom continued to care for her, and he and Mr. St. Clare rarely left her bedside.

Eva gave all of the slaves a curl of her hair. She entreated them to pray every day and to be good. Eva also asked her father to give Tom his freedom after she died. Mr. St. Clare agreed.

Eventually the fateful day came. The whole house felt the loss of the bright, happy little girl. Mr. St. Clare took her death particularly hard. He spent much of his time with Tom. Tom was as devoted to his master as he had been to Eva. Mr. St. Clare told Tom that he was in the process of freeing him. Tom declared that even if he had his freedom he wouldn't leave until Mr. St. Clare no longer needed him.

The entire household was shocked when Mr. St. Clare died in an accident just a short time later.

10

Plural Nouns

Read the nouns below. Write the plural forms in the blanks provided.

foot	_feet_	enemy	_enemies_	flock	_flocks_
country	_countries_	woman	_women_	rash	_rashes_
sheep	_sheep_	berry	_berries_	life	_lives_
couch	_couches_	roof	_roofs_	hoof	_hooves_

11

Edit this passage from *Uncle Tom's Cabin*. Cross out any misspelled plural nouns and write the correct plural nouns above.

There are 16 errors in this passage.

Mrs. St. Clare did not have the same compassion for slaves that her husband and daughter had shared. After Mr. St. Clare's death, she announced that they were all going to be sold at an auction. Mr. St. Clare had not yet given Tom his freedom, and Mrs. St. Clare refused to honor her husband's [wishes].

A plantation owner named Simon Legree bought Tom and another slave named Emmeline. He owned several [properties] by the Red River. Legree was a cold-hearted, ruthless man who worked his slaves to death and then bought more. He had made two of his [men], Sambo and Quimbo, overseers. The overseers had been trained to hate the other slaves, and they disciplined them mercilessly.

When Tom arrived at the plantation, he found that Legree's character had influenced everyone on the plantation. The other slaves were selfish and hard-hearted. They didn't help or care about each other. Tom soon began to have an impact on the abused [people]. He helped the weaker ones meet their quota and make their meals. He told everyone about Jesus.

12

93

Verbs

Circle all of the verbs in the sentences below. Identify them as action (a), linking (l), or helping (h) verbs.

The worms were wriggling across the sidewalk. (helping, action)

The lasagna smelled delicious. (linking)

I am embarrassed. (linking)

The baker placed a fresh batch of cookies in the display. (action)

He should have asked for directions. (helping, helping, action)

Mom had driven to the store. (helping, action)

13

Read this passage from *Uncle Tom's Cabin*. Identify the underlined verbs as action (a), helping (h), or linking (l) verbs.

Simon Legree was not pleased with Tom's performance. While Tom was(l) a very hard worker, he was not the sort of slave Legree wanted. He had(h) been(h) hoping(a) to make Tom his top over-seer, but Tom was too nice to the other slaves. Legree decided to start training him to be mean. One evening he ordered Tom to whip one of his fellow workers. Tom refused(a).

"I will(h) work(a) day and night, Master," he said, "but I won't whip any men or women. It just isn't right to be so cruel."

Legree was(l) furious! He ordered Sambo and Quimbo to whip Tom until he learned his place.

Tom was left broken and bleeding in an isolated shed. One of the slaves from the house, Cassy, brought(a) him some water and treated his wounds. Cassy had(h) lived(a) on the plantation for many years, and her misery had slowly turned into anger. She hated Legree and had long forsaken any trust in God.

Before Tom's wounds had healed, Legree ordered(a) him back to work. Tom's life became(l) a wearying cycle of toil and pain.

14

Review Time!

Edit this passage from *Uncle Tom's Cabin*.
There are 11 errors in this passage.

One day Cassy told Tom that she had decided to try and escape. No one had ever managed to escape from Legree's plantation before, but Cassy had a clever plan. There was an empty room on the top floor of Legree's house. One of Legree's slaves had died in the room, and now everyone believed that it was haunted. Legree himself was scared to death of the room, for his guilt interfered with his reason. Cassy had been stockpiling [supplies] in that very room. She and Emmeline were going to leave the house and run to the [marshes] at a time when someone would be sure to see them. While Legree and the overseers struggled to free the dogs and get their horses, the [women] would circle back through the creek and return to the house. They would stay in the room for a few days until Legree stopped looking for them, and then they would escape in earnest at night. Cassy knew that no one would ever think to look for them in the house, and nobody would go anywhere close to the room.

Cassy urged Tom to escape with them, but Tom said he couldn't.

"I have a work to do among these poor souls," he explained. "I just can't leave them now."

15

Verb Tenses

Identify the complete tense of each verb/verb phrase underlined below.

They are catching lightning bugs.   present progressive

Joyce will walk home after the picnic.   simple future

I have opened the gift from Grandma.   present perfect

The wind was ruffling my hair.   past progressive

We shall have finished our supper.   future perfect

16

94

Read this passage from *Uncle Tom's Cabin*. Identify the complete tense of each underlined verb/verb phrase.

On the day that Cassy and Emmeline faked their escape, everything went according to Cassy's plan. Legree, Sambo, and Quimbo looked and looked for the women, but they could find no trace of them. Legree threatened to kill Tom if he didn't tell him where the women were hiding (past progressive).

"I will not tell (simple future) you," Tom said. "They are trusting (present progressive) in me."

Legree commanded the two overseers to whip Tom, and he stood by and watched (simple past). He threatened and cursed and yelled at Tom, but Tom bore his punishment with patience. He felt a deep peace, for he knew he was going (past progressive) home. Just before Tom fainted, he told Legree that he forgave him. Legree looked at Tom's unconscious body and walked away. As soon as their master had left (past perfect), Quimbo and Sambo knelt (simple past) down by Tom and revived him. They had been touched by his faith and perseverance, and they cried and asked him to forgive them. Tom prayed with the two savage men.

Two days later a man came to Legree's plantation looking for Tom. It was Mr. Shelby's son, George Shelby. Five years had passed (past perfect) since Tom had been sold, and George had come to buy him back.

17

Irregular Verbs

Students probably know and use most irregular verbs already. However, some of them might be a little tricky. To familiarize students with irregular verbs, use a basic framework for them to repeat the verb in the present tense, past tense, and past participle. For example, with the irregular verb "drive," the student would say "Today I drive; yesterday I drove; yesterday I had driven." Reading the sentence out loud often helps students remember or recognize the correct form of the verb.

Write the past tense and past participle of each present tense verb.

(begin)   Yesterday I __began__ typing.   I had __begun__ typing.
(come)   Yesterday I __came__ home.   I had __come__ home.
(get)   Yesterday I __got__ a car.   I had __gotten__ a car.
(shake)   Yesterday I __shook__ his hand. I had __shaken__ his hand.
(throw)   Yesterday I __threw__ a fit.   I had __thrown__ a fit.

18

Read this passage from *Uncle Tom's Cabin*. Cross out any incorrect irregular verbs and write the correct verbs above.

There are 7 incorrect irregular verbs in this passage.

George [found] Tom lying in a shed.

"I have [come] to take you home, Tom," George said.

"It does my heart good to see you," Tom replied, "but you're too late. The Lord is going to take me home."

Tom was overcome with joy and peace. He died just a few moments later. George wrapped his cloak around the faithful slave and buried him.

The next day Cassy and Emmeline [ran] away. They ended up boarding the same boat as George Shelby. There was another woman on the boat who was trying to find George Harris. She was his sister. Cassy [heard] George telling the woman about George and Eliza Harris, and she couldn't believe it. Eliza was her daughter! Cassy had [given] up hope of ever seeing her again. George Shelby directed them all to where the Harris family lived, and they had a tearful reunion.

As for George Shelby, he [went] home to share the news of Tom's death. The slaves were deeply saddened, but they were overjoyed when George [gave] them their freedom. While standing by Uncle Tom's grave, he had resolved never to own another slave again.

19

Review Time!

Edit this passage from *Frankenstein*.

There are 13 errors in this passage.

I was stranded with my sled on a large piece of ice. All but one of my dogs had died; the open sea surrounded me. Suddenly I [saw] a ship! I had thought that circumstance to be impossible this far north, yet there it was. Using pieces of my sled as oars, I struggled until I reached the side of the vessel. The crew members, shocked at my appearance, begged me to come on board and be saved. When I [found] out they were heading north, I agreed to board the ship.

Due to fatigue and hardship, I fainted with illness. When I had recovered enough to communicate, I learned that the captain had been most attentive to my needs. I introduced myself as Victor Frankenstein. His name was Robert Walton. We [spent] much time talking, and I soon discovered his purpose in sailing to the North Pole. Robert was filled with lofty aspirations and dreams of glory. This same trait in myself had [led] only to pain and destruction. I decided to share my story with Robert in hopes that it would make a difference.

20

95

Subject / Verb Agreement

It may help students to read the sentences out loud.

Circle the correct verbs in the sentences below.

My grandma (sit / sits) on the couch. I (sit / sits) on the chair.

We (is / are) going to the mountains. My cousin (is / are) going with us.

Either my cat or her kittens (eat / eats) too much.

Louis and his brother (sell / sells) produce. Louis (sell / sells) more.

Mom (allow / allows) me to go swimming. Will you (allow / allows) it?

21

Edit this passage from *Frankenstein*. Circle the correct verbs.

There are 12 errors in this passage.

My father, Alphonse Frankenstein, had married a kind, virtuous woman named Caroline, whom he had saved from poverty. I (was / were) their firstborn son. When I was still young, my parents adopted a beautiful orphan girl. Her name was Elizabeth, and I loved her dearly. We (was / were) very close in age, and our [personalities] complemented each other wonderfully. As we grew up, I became very interested in science. I was especially curious about the secret of life. I often thought of the glory I could attain if could stop all but violent deaths.

I had only one friend. His name was Henry Clerval, and we were as close as brothers. When I (was / were) seven years old, my mother bore another son, Ernest. Little William came next. When was seventeen, my mother died of scarlet fever. I [left] soon after to continue my education at a university. I missed my family and Henry, but I was eager to further my knowledge of science.

22

Verbals

Identify the types of verbals underlined in the sentences below.

She tried to sleep on the plane, but she couldn't. ___infinitive___

I returned the carton of cracked eggs to the store. ___participle___

To keep a secret isn't easy. ___infinitive___

The mob of cheering fans rushed onto the field. ___participle___

My mom dislikes shopping. ___gerund___

Gardening is hard work. ___gerund___

23

Read this passage from *Frankenstein*. Identify the underlined verbals as gerunds (g), infinitives (i), or participles (p).

Among other things I studied chemistry and anatomy. I was so engrossed in these studies that I advanced very quickly and became somewhat of an expert in only two years. Learning(g) absorbed all of my energies, and I finally discovered how to create life. The next step was to make(i) a man and give him life. I decided to make an extraordinary man, eight feet tall and very strong. After more than a year of working(g), my creation was finished. I gathered my instruments and gave him the spark of life.

His eyes opened, he began to breathe(i), and his limbs shook. In that moment I was overcome with horror. He was hideous! His shaggy hair, watery eyes, pale skin, and dark lips disgusted me when I saw them move. I fled from the room and lay on my bed, where I fell into a troubled(p) sleep. Instead of something glorious, had created a dreadful monster!

When I awoke, the monster was leaning over my bed. I ran out of the house, for I was sickened by the sight of my living(p) creation.

24

96

Review Time!	**Pronouns**

Review Time!

Edit this passage from *Frankenstein*. Identify the underlined verbals as gerunds (g), infinitives (i), or participles (p).

There are 9 errors in this passage.

My good friend, Henry Clerval, arrived the very next day. I was so pleased to see(i) him that I forgot all about my horrible creation until he arrived at my door. Fortunately, the created(p) monster had left. Due to sickness and other circumstances, another couple of years passed before I returned home. Returning(g) was bittersweet; my youngest brother, William, had been murdered. He had turned up missing while playing outside, and my family had spent hours searching for him. His body was found the next morning. He had been strangled, and the locket with our mother's picture had been [taken] from his neck.

When I arrived home, I went to visit(i) the place where William's body had been found. Just then, a flash of lightning lit up the sky. In the distance I saw a tall, hideous figure. It was the monster! I hadn't seen him in years, but I knew right then that he (was / were) responsible for my brother's death.

25

Pronouns

Circle all of the pronouns in the sentences below.

All is not lost. We still have a chance. Everyone must keep trying.
These are delicious. Did you make them? None will be left.
Nora and I are going on a trip to Italy. We paid for it ourselves.
What is the matter? Nobody knows. That is the problem.

26

Edit this passage from *Frankenstein*. Circle the correct pronouns.

There are 10 errors in this passage.

I soon learned that one of our most trusted servants, Justine Moritz, had been accused of the crime. The locket had been found in the pocket of her dress. (She / Her) ardently denied the charges, but the evidence against (she / her) was too strong. I had no way of proving her innocence; my story was too far-fetched. No one would believe that (I / me) had [made] a monstrous man. Despite my best efforts, Justine was executed for murder.

I knew that both of these deaths were my fault; I had given life to the wretched creature responsible for taking their [lives]. I [fell] into a deep despair that my dear family couldn't understand. They too were hurting, yet I was isolated by the burden of my terrible secret. I went to the mountains to spend some time alone. While I was there, the monster approached (I / me). I wanted to fight him to the death, but (he / him) pleaded with me to listen to his story. He claimed to have been a peaceful creature before experiencing the rejection and hatred of man. I followed (he / him) to his hut, where he shared his tale.

27

Pronoun / Antecedent Agreement

Circle the correct pronouns in the sentences below.

There are three bowls on the table. (It / They) are filled with soup.
That little boy lives across the street. (He / She) is eight years old.
The girl picked out ten books. (She / They) read (it / them) all.
We went camping. We cooked the food (himself / ourselves).
Libby mowed the lawn. (It / They) took (him / her) a long time.

28

97

97

Edit this passage from *Frankenstein*. Circle the correct pronouns.

There are 9 errors in this passage.

The monster had stumbled away from my house his first night with only a cloak. (She / He) had no knowledge of day and night, land and water, or food and sleep. He passed several days in a forest, where he ate nuts and [berries]. His first encounters with humans did not go well, so he fled to a place of seclusion. He found an abandoned kennel behind an isolated home in the country, and (he / they) made it his home. A French family lived in the cottage, and he [grew] to love (they / them). Although he kept himself hidden, he spent a great deal of time watching and learning from them. In time he could understand their language, read, and even speak. Eventually he decided to approach the family. Instead of accepting (them / him), they (was / were) terrified and chased him away. Deeply hurt, he fled once again.

The monster had [found] some of my papers in the cloak. He decided to try and find (him / me). Meanwhile, anger and hatred began to grow inside of him. He yearned for revenge against (I / me) and my race, for we had rejected him.

29

Review Time!

Edit this passage from *Frankenstein*.

There are 10 errors in this passage.

The creature [came] upon little William by chance. Learning that (he / him) was my brother, the monster had killed him. He wanted to hurt me, for I was his creator and yet had not accepted him.

When the monster finished his tale, he told me he wanted me to create a mate for (him / them). He wanted only what humans enjoyed and yet would not give him - acceptance. Once I [gave] him his mate, he promised they would travel to a remote place and never bother another human again. If (I / me) did not make him a mate, he threatened to continue bringing destruction upon the human race, especially against me and my family. Although I hesitated to make another creature capable of such destruction, I decided that I could not allow (him / her) to torment my fellow human beings. I agreed, and (we / us) parted.

In the days that followed, my father approached me about Elizabeth. My parents had always hoped we would one day wed, and he thought that our union would bring happiness to the household again. My dear Elizabeth and I set the date for the next year.

30

Apostrophes

Possessives ending with "s" can be tricky. If a singular noun ends with an "s" or a "z" sound, you may just add an apostrophe. However, there is one exception. If a singular noun ending with "s" is a one-syllable word, it requires both an apostrophe and "s." **That is Les's house.**

Add apostrophes where they belong in the sentences below.
I can't believe spring is finally here. It's Mom's favorite season. She's at her grandparents' house. They don't live very far away. This is Alex's room. It's very clean. We'll sleep here tonight. You've heard of the Northern Lights, haven't you? They're beautiful. I'm the owner of four ducks. That is the ducks' food.

31

Edit this passage from *Frankenstein*.

There are 12 errors in this passage.

In the meantime I set off to fulfill my promise. I [told] my family that I wanted to travel before settling down in marriage. In truth I needed to do some more studying before I could create a mate for the monster. I wanted to fulfill my obligation so that I could focus on Elizabeth's happiness.

Henry Clerval, my childhood friend, accompanied me in my travels. After many months we parted ways. I could finally begin my work. I chose a secluded hut where I wouldn't be discovered and set forth to create life again. What I had accomplished with enthusiasm three years earlier, I now toiled at with disgust. The monster had warned (I / me) that he would be watching, and I had no doubt that he'd followed me closely.

Indeed, on the very night I completed his mate, the creature was watching me through the window. The monster's terrible appearance horrified me so much that I couldn't bring myself to give life to another like him. I tore my new creation to pieces!

32

98

Commas

or the first rule, using commas in a series, students are taught to use
ommas after each item. However, students may notice some writers omit
e last comma (before "and"). This is not technically wrong, but it is
ecoming more and more common to use a comma here. It also helps
ake the sentence clearer, so it is a good habit for students to learn.
mphasize to students that commas are not needed if all of the words in
series are connected by the word "and."

dd commas where they belong in the sentences below.
asketball, the best sport ever, was invented by Dr. Naismith.
ave you made any new friends, Becky?
ids, do you want ketchup, mustard, and onions on your hotdogs?
have a hockey game, by the way, on Tuesday night.
randma, my mom's mom, is arriving Friday, Saturday, or Sunday.

Edit this passage from *Frankenstein* by adding commas where they belong.

There are 11 errors in this passage.

Later that night the monster entered my room, walked up to me, and demanded to know why I had destroyed his mate. I told him that I refused to carry out my promise.

"Shall every creature have a mate except for me?" he questioned me. "Am I to be left alone while you live in happiness?"

"Leave me, monster!" I replied. "I will not change my mind!"

"I will leave you for now, but I will be there on your wedding night," the monster threatened. With those final words, he disappeared into the night.

I shuddered, closed the door, and set about packing up my things. He had told me that he would come on my wedding night; I resolved to be ready. I would not let him kill me without a fight. I could not stand the thought of leaving Elizabeth, the woman I loved, alone. I decided I would kill the monster before he could kill me.

An unforeseen event shook me yet again. The body of Henry Clerval, my closest friend, was found by some villagers. He had been strangled. The monster was punishing me, I realized, for breaking my word.

Review Time!

dit this passage from *Frankenstein*.

here are 18 errors in this passage.

I returned home with a heavy heart. Elizabeth greeted me with ears in her eyes. She had lost weight, sleep, and joy over the nhappy events of the last couple of years.

Fearing that the monster might kill another innocent human if (I / e) postponed my marriage, I began to make preparations. I arried pistols, knives, and other weapons. I was determined to be eady when the monster returned.

Our wedding day arrived, and we enjoyed a quiet ceremony. fterwards, we traveled to Lakeside Inn, a small hotel on the lake. y thoughts were focused on the monster's threat. If only I could ake it through one more night, it seemed, then Elizabeth and I ould be free to live in happiness.

That night I encouraged Elizabeth, my new bride, to retire to our oom. I didn't want her to witness what I knew was coming. I alked around the outside of the inn, searching for any sign of the onster's arrival.

Elizabeth's shrill scream suddenly echoed from our room! When I urst in the door, Elizabeth's lifeless body was lying on the bed. he had been strangled!

Commas

A comma may or may not be used if an introductory phrase is short, so please note that there may be times when students feel a comma is needed and it is not shown (or vice versa).

Add commas where they belong in the sentences below.
After eating too much ice cream, I had an upset stomach.
Well, do you want to come over tomorrow?
My brother is taller than I am but not as strong.
The short, round clowns weren't as funny as the three tall clowns.
Haven hates to shell peas, but I think it is fun.

Edit this passage from *Frankenstein* by adding commas where they belong.

There are 9 errors in this passage.

I returned home in despair. My father was unable to bear the horrible, unexpected news of Elizabeth's death, and he died within a few days. The monster had taken away my family, yet I lived. I had never even imagined that he might carry out his revenge in this way!

I vowed to track the monster down and destroy him. This, it seemed, was what he wanted, for he managed to keep me close on his trail without ever letting me get close enough to kill him. For seven lonely months I followed him in hopes of destroying him. He led me north to this very place. That was why I agreed to board your ship only after learning that you were traveling northward.

Thus I ended my story, and Robert Walton and I sat in silence.

After hearing Victor Frankenstein's story, I felt unimaginable compassion for him. I did my best to take care of him, but his health failed daily. He died on my ship, free at last from the trouble caused by his ambitions.

37

Semi-Colons

Add commas and semi-colons where they belong in the sentences below.

My birthday is next week; I got a card today.

Trisha went to the park; Leeann went with her.

I left my shoes by the door, for they were very dirty.

He opened the mailbox and saw there was nothing inside.

We didn't have any eggs, so I went to the grocery store.

The rodeo was very exciting; the bull riding was a little scary.

I have a dentist appointment on Thursday; a recital, softball game, and slumber party on Friday; and a babysitting job on Saturday.

38

Edit this passage from *The Black Arrow* by adding commas and semi-colons where they belong.

There are 13 errors in this passage.

A bell rang out across Tunstall one afternoon in late spring. The small village was surrounded by forest; had a dozen or so houses, a great moat-house, and a church; and was home to a handful of families. The people of Tunstall left their work and gathered around the moathouse to find out why the bell had rung.

The question was answered by Richard Shelton, a boy of almost eighteen. Richard's guardian was Sir Daniel Brackley, the lord and knight of Tunstall. There was an upcoming battle between the houses of Lancaster and York; Sir Brackley needed more men. Sir Brackley had been known to change his loyalties more than once in order to profit personally, but Richard Shelton was loyal to his guardian nevertheless.

An old veteran, Nick Appleyard, was assigned to stay and defend Tunstall with seven men. The rest would join Sir Brackley in Kettley. Richard and Bennet Hatch, Sir Brackley's second-in-command, explained the situation to Nick Appleyard. As they stood talking, an arrow whistled through the air and killed Appleyard. The arrow was completely black.

39

Review Time!

Edit this passage from *The Black Arrow*.

There are 16 errors in this passage.

Richard and Bennet returned to the moathouse. They told the villagers what had happened. Meanwhile, a paper had been found nailed to the door of Holywood Abbey, the church. It was a poem of warning to four men. The first was Nick Appleyard, who had already been killed. The second was Bennet Hatch. The third was Oliver Oates, a priest and close friend of Sir Daniel Brackley. Lastly, the poem named Sir Brackley himself. The poem spoke of four black arrows that would pierce the four black hearts of these men. The poem also blamed these men for the death of Sir Harry Shelton, Richard's father. Richard was naturally curious; he determined to find out who was responsible for killing his father.

It was decided that Richard would lead the new recruits to join Brackley. They arrived in Kettley later that night. Brackley sent Richard back to Tunstall with a message for Bennet Hatch. Richard was disappointed that he would not be fighting in the battle, but he obeyed his guardian.

40

100

Quotes

Please note that when students are editing, missing quotation marks count as only one error although students will always add them in pairs.

Add capital letters and punctuation to the sentences below.

"Wow!" Colin yelled. "Did you see that?"

The doctor said, "Make sure you rest." "I will," I replied.

Tom asked if we wanted some hot cocoa.

"I'm going to take a picture," my brother said. "Say cheese!"

41

Edit this passage from *The Black Arrow*.

There are 15 errors in this passage.

About a mile from Kettley, Richard heard someone call to him. A boy a little bit younger than himself stepped out from behind some weeds. He begged Richard to lead him to Holywood Abbey. Richard agreed to help him, and he let the boy ride his horse while he walked alongside.

At Richard's prodding, the boy introduced himself.

"My name is John Matcham," the boy said. "I am sixteen years old."

John explained that he was fleeing from Sir Brackley. Brackley had taken John by force. John had escaped and was desperate to reach the safety of Holywood. Richard vowed to lead John safely to the church; the boys quickly became good friends.

John told Richard that Sir Brackley planned to marry Richard to a girl named Joanna Sedley for his own profit. John also spoke to Richard about Sir Brackley's role in the death of Richard's father. John didn't understand why Richard defended Sir Brackley. Richard replied that he didn't know the facts, and until he did he would remain loyal to the man who had raised him.

42

Edit this passage from *The Black Arrow*.

There are 11 errors in this passage.

As the two boys continued through the woods, they spied a man keeping watch in a tree. They chose a different path, but they heard another man singing. Spying some ruins, they hid themselves well. The man came around the corner, and soon he was joined by a large band of men. (They / Them) were the men of the black arrow, and they were talking about their plans to kill Sir Daniel. A signal sounded; the men ran to their various stations. John and Richard came out of their hiding place. Richard wanted to warn Sir Daniel and his men, but John did not. He pleaded with Richard to continue on to Holywood. Despite John's pleading, Richard set off to warn his friends. He was too late to help them, and he was seen by one of the men of the black arrow. The boys again [ran] into the woods to hide.

Sir Brackley had disguised himself as a blind leper to escape from the men of the black arrow. He found the boys and took them to Tunstall.

43

Edit this passage from *The Black Arrow*.

There are 16 errors in this passage.

Once in Tunstall Richard was separated from John. He was curious what became of the boy, but he was more curious about who had killed his father. When Sir Brackley heard about Richard's doubts, he called his ward in for a talk. Richard asked his guardian if he had any part in the death of Sir Shelton, but Sir Brackley denied it. He said that he was hurt by Richard's suspicions. Still, Richard believed the knight was lying.

That night John snuck into Richard's room. He warned Richard that he had heard some men making plans to kill Richard! Just then the boys heard a loud cry followed by shouts for Joanna.

John crumbled. "I am lost!" he cried. "We must flee!"

Richard was confused. It took him only a moment to understand. "You're Joanna?" he asked. He stood for a moment and then spoke again.

"Joanna, we have both saved the other's life," he said, "and if I live, I will indeed marry you gladly!"

44

101

Midterm

Edit this passage from *The Black Arrow*.

There are 14 errors in this passage.

Richard and Joanna slipped down a secret passageway. They entered a room where a long rope [hung] out the window. At that moment several men barged into the room. They had been found! Joanna fainted, but Richard managed to escape out of the window. He swam across the moat and ran to safety. He knew that Sir Daniel would not harm Joanna, for he would profit richly from her marriage. Richard vowed to rescue her as soon as possible.

Richard was found by some men of the black arrow. They took (him / them) to their leader, Ellis Duckworth.

"Don't worry, dear boy," Ellis reassured him. "You are now in the hands of someone who loved your father. I have vowed to avenge his death."

Richard had escaped from his deceitful guardian and was now among true friends. The men of the black arrow had been friends of his father. Richard joined them and [became] a respected leader.

45

Adjectives

Circle all of the adjectives in the sentences below.

Many tourists go to Florida towns to enjoy the warm weather.

Stephanie's bowling team got a better score than that team.

We went to a popular Mexican restaurant; the food was delicious.

Those three boys aren't wearing any shoes.

46

Read this passage from *The Black Arrow*. Circle as many adjectives as you can find.

Many months passed. The long war between the Lancaster and York houses continued. Sir Brackley fought for the Lancaster side, while Richard had joined the York party. Joanna was still in Sir Brackley's care, and Richard thought about her often. One day Richard learned that his lovely Joanna was to be married to Lord Shoreby.

Richard set off for the large town of Shoreby to find Joanna. Early one morning he heard a loud trumpet followed by the distinct clash of swords. He ran towards the sound and came upon a lone man in a desperate fight against seven others. Richard immediately jumped into the fight. After several moments of intense fighting, a band of men appeared and the fierce attackers ran away.

Richard had come to the aid of the Duke of Gloucester, an important leader of the York party.

47

Edit this passage from *The Black Arrow*.

There are 13 errors in this passage.

The Duke of Gloucester was very grateful to Richard. His band of men had responded to his trumpet call too late to help him. If Richard hadn't come to his rescue, he would have been killed.

The Duke of Gloucester was leading his men to Shoreby, where they would fight against the Lancaster forces. The duke made Richard a commander, and they devised a plan of attack. They would first seize a portion of the city, where they would set up their defense. They needed to hold the Lancaster forces back until more York reinforcements arrived.

After taking a quarter of the city by surprise and force, Richard and the men under his command were assigned a street to defend. It didn't take long for the Lancaster forces to prepare themselves, and then the battle began in earnest. Richard and his men fought valiantly. Just as Richard felt sure (they / them) could last no longer, the York reinforcements arrived. The Lancaster party scattered, and the battle was [won].

48

102

Edit this passage from *The Black Arrow*.

There are 11 errors in this passage.

The duke was extremely pleased with Richard's bravery and leadership. He knighted Richard, dubbing him Sir Richard. Afterwards, Richard went to the house where Sir Brackley had been keeping Joanna. The house was a mess! It had been completely ransacked; men were swarming into it and carrying out anything of value. Richard ran inside, but neither Sir Brackley nor Joanna (was / were) anywhere to be seen. Finding an archer who had been there when the house was taken, Richard learned that Sir Brackley had fled with twenty or so others. Whether Joanna had been among them, the archer [knew] not.

Richard returned to the Duke of Gloucester. He asked for some men to take in pursuit of Sir Brackley. The duke agreed, and Richard set off with fifty men. They followed the trail left by Sir Brackley and his companions. Late in the evening Richard and his men [came] upon the campfire of Sir Brackley. Richard realized too late that Sir Brackley's men had scattered and now surrounded them!

49

Edit this passage from *The Black Arrow*.

There are 12 errors in this passage.

Richard's men immediately began to retreat. In the midst of the confusion, Joanna jumped off of her horse and [ran] to Richard's side. Seeing that they had only one chance of survival, Richard and Joanna fled into the forest.

They came to Holywood Abbey in Tunstall just a few hours later. As he had promised so long ago, Richard brought Joanna safely to the church. They agreed to wed the very next day.

Early in the morning Richard went out for a walk. Just before (he / him) turned back to the church, he saw a lone man. It was Sir Brackley, defeated and forlorn. Richard decided to let Sir Brackley live, but a black arrow whistled through the air and killed him. It was the arrow of Ellis Duckworth, who had finally taken his revenge for the death of Sir Shelton.

Richard and Joanna were married that same day. They became the new lord and lady of Tunstall, and they stayed in the great moathouse. There they lived in happiness, free from the [miseries] of war.

50

Adverbs

Some words can function as adverbs or prepositions. If it is an adverb, it will not be followed by a noun or a pronoun. For example, in the sentence "He looked **out**," "out" is an adverb. In the sentence "He looked **out** the window," "out" is a preposition because it is followed by a noun, "window." Adverbs often come right before prepositions, as in the sentence, "He looked **out** of the window." Students should understand this before trying to find the adverbs on the next page (52). They will get more practice and direction on the prepositions page (56).

It is important that students understand that "not" is an adverb because it is very common and is often buried in a contraction.

Complete the sentences below by writing adverbs in the blanks.
Answers will vary.

He laughs ___quietly, easily___ .   You swim ___slowly, wonderfully___ .
This was ___well, poorly___ written.   She ___rarely, always___ travels .
That dog snarled ferociously. This one growled ___more ferociously___ .
I know she sings well, but does she sing ___better___ than you?

51

Read this passage from *The Scarlet Pimpernel*. Circle as many adverbs as you can find.

The city of Paris was in turmoil in September of 1792. The French Revolution had quickly turned the streets of Paris into an endless scene of death. The common people had tired of living in poverty and oppression, and they had finally overthrown the rich nobles and aristocrats who ruled over France. Now the peasants ruthlessly sentenced dozens of aristocrats to death daily. The commoners watched the executions.

Another favorite sport of the common people was to go to the barricades, for aristocrats tried to escape fairly often. On this day there were many women leaving the city. They pushed carts for selling their goods at the market nearby. The guards carefully checked each cart. As one of the guards approached the cart of an ugly old woman, she cackled loudly and casually mentioned that her grandson had smallpox. The guard quickly backed away, yelling angrily at the ugly old woman.

The old woman was a man in disguise. He was using the cart to cleverly rescue three aristocrats from France.

52

Edit this passage from *The Scarlet Pimpernel*.

There are 15 errors in this passage.

   The three aristocrats and the man who had saved them made it safely to an inn in England, where (they / them) were free. The man belonged to a small group of men who risked their [lives] to rescue the nobles of France. The leader of this group was known only as the Scarlet Pimpernel. His real identity was a mystery.

   Two other guests happened to be staying at that very same inn. They were Sir Percy Blakeney and his wife, Lady Marguerite Blakeney. Sir Percy was one of the richest men in England, and he was quite tall and very strong. He would have been called handsome if not for the dull, lazy expression always on his face. He was known for his inane chatter and quick, constant laugh.

   His wife, on the other hand, was both very beautiful and exceedingly smart. She was from France, and everyone was surprised when she married such a dull man. Lady Blakeney grew tired of her husband's meaningless chatter and laugh, but his devotion could not be faulted.

Edit this passage from *The Scarlet Pimpernel*.

There are 13 errors in this passage.

   One fine autumn evening the Blakeneys attended a ball in London. It was hosted by Lord Grenville. Sir Percy and Lady Marguerite Blakeney were quite respected by English society. They were very rich and always impeccably dressed in the latest fashions.

   Although Lady Blakeney usually enjoyed social functions, she knew that she would not have a good time on this particular night. One of her old acquaintances from France, a man by the name of Chauvelin, was also at the ball. He was trying to catch the Scarlet Pimpernel. Chauvelin had forced Lady Blakeney into helping him. Her brother had been discovered to be part of the League of the Scarlet Pimpernel, and Chauvelin had promised that he would go free if Lady Blakeney helped to gather information. Marguerite had been torn between her respect for the brave man who was rescuing so many of her countrymen and her love for her only brother.

   In the end Marguerite [knew] that she could not sentence her brother to death. She saw a note from the Scarlet Pimpernel and passed the information on to Chauvelin.

Edit this passage from *The Scarlet Pimpernel*.

There are 12 errors in this passage.

   Lady Blakeney [felt] guilty. She was desperate to talk with someone, so she decided to open up to her husband. However, as soon as she saw Percy with his lazy grin and annoying laugh, she knew he would be of no help. Sighing, she climbed up beside him on the coach for the trip home.

   Although Sir Percy had loved Lady Marguerite deeply at one time, something had changed after they'd gotten married. He had found out about something in Marguerite's past. Before they'd been married, she had spoken harshly against a fellow Frenchman. In the current, uncertain times, her words had been used at a trial. The aristocrat and his entire family were sentenced to death. Marguerite had been horrified, but it didn't change her role in their deaths. It was true that Sir Percy lavished his riches upon Lady Marguerite and was a devoted husband, but the love was gone. Despite her indifference towards Percy for most of their relationship, Lady Marguerite now realized how much she loved and missed (he / him).

Prepositions

   In order for students to tell whether a prepositional phrase functions as an adjective or an adverb, they should find the word it modifies. If it modifies a noun or pronoun, the prepositional phrase functions as an adjective. If it modifies a verb, adjective, or adverb, it functions as an adverb.

Underline the prepositional phrases. Identify them as adjectival or adverbial.

It rains often in the spring.	adverbial
Oranges from Florida are delicious.	adjectival
The man in the blue Illinois cap is my dad.	adjectival
He drank some water and then ran outside.	no prep. phrase
I put the photos in an album.	adverbial

Read this passage from *The Scarlet Pimpernel*. Underline the prepositional phrases and circle the objects of the prepositions.

The next morning Lady Blakeney woke early after a short night of troubled sleep. She found a note from her husband; it said that he was leaving on unexpected business. He would be back within a week.

Marguerite got dressed and wandered around the house. She mused about her relationship with her husband and determined to fix things when he got back. As she passed his private study, she was overcome with curiosity. In all honesty, she had never before cared about the contents of this secretive room. Sir Percy usually kept the room locked, but today the door was open. Marguerite glanced around cautiously and entered.

The room was simply furnished. There were two maps of France on the wall, and a portrait of Sir Percy's mother hung by the desk. As Marguerite turned to leave, she accidentally sent a small object rolling across the floor. She picked it up and gasped. It was a solid gold ring, and it displayed the symbol of the Scarlet Pimpernel. Her husband was the mysterious hero!

Edit this passage from *The Scarlet Pimpernel*. Identify the underlined prepositional phrases as adjectival (adj.) or adverbial (adv.).

There are 14 errors in this passage.

Lady Blakeney could hardly believe it, yet she knew it was true. She realized all at once that Sir Percy's dull, lazy expression was simply a mask. Indeed, she was sure no one would ever suspect that her husband was the courageous, daring leader known as the Scarlet Pimpernel.

It didn't take Marguerite long to realize the danger she had unknowingly placed upon her husband (adv. - modifies placed). By giving the information to Chauvelin and protecting her brother, she had betrayed her own husband! He had already left for France, and now she knew he was going to rescue more aristocrats. Chauvelin was probably following him. Once they were in France (adv. - modifies were), the Frenchman would arrest Sir Percy. Then Percy would be sentenced to death!

Marguerite knew she had to warn her husband. She [left] at once for the home of Sir Andrew Ffoulkes (adj. - modifies home), her husband's good friend. She had correctly guessed that he was part of the League of the Scarlet Pimpernel (adj. - modifies League), and she explained the situation to (he / him). They too left for France.

Edit this passage from *The Scarlet Pimpernel.*

There are 15 errors in this passage.

Lady Marguerite and Sir Andrew arrived at a certain inn in France. Sir Andrew told Marguerite that it was a common stop for the Scarlet Pimpernel and his men. Indeed, the innkeeper told them that a tall Englishman had been there not long before. Sir Andrew went out to look for Sir Percy, and Lady Marguerite stayed at the inn. She [sat] in a room upstairs where (she / they) could watch the main room unnoticed.

The door opened. It was Chauvelin! He talked with the innkeeper and then sat down to eat. Lady Marguerite was trapped! She couldn't warn her husband without revealing herself to Chauvelin. All she could do was sit and hope that Sir Percy would not return to the inn.

One of Chauvelin's men, Desgas, came in to report to Chauvelin. He told his master that the streets were all heavily guarded. The men were waiting; they were watching for any tall stranger.

Edit this passage from *The Scarlet Pimpernel.*

There are 12 errors in this passage.

Desgas returned with a dirty, elderly Jewish man a short while later. The man had some information for Chauvelin. He and another Jew had met a tall Englishman less than an hour before. The Englishman had [bought] a horse and cart from them and then had started towards a certain fisherman's hut on the beach.

Chauvelin was thrilled at the news! He gathered as much information as he could from the Jewish man. Then he ordered the man to show him the way to the fisherman's hut. They left the inn and disappeared into the night. Lady Blakeney had heard everything. She put on her cloak, quietly slipped out of the inn, and followed the men. Keeping to the shadows, she followed as closely as possible without being seen.

A group of soldiers met Chauvelin and the Jew on the road. They had some news for Chauvelin; they had found the fisherman's hut. There were several men inside, and they appeared to be waiting for something.

Direct and Indirect Objects

Identify any direct objects (DO) or indirect objects (IO) in the sentences below.

Caroline gave her dog (IO) a bath (DO) last week.

The child drew his dad (IO) a picture (DO) of a big red truck.

Will you tell me (IO) a story (DO)?

He opened and read the letter (DO) immediately.

Edit this passage from *The Scarlet Pimpernel*. Identify any direct or indirect objects in the underlined sentences.

There are 12 errors in this passage.

Chauvelin understood exactly what was happening. The men in the hut were aristocrats, and they were waiting for the Scarlet Pimpernel to come for them. Chauvelin gave his men (IO) very strict orders (DO). They were to keep watch around the fisherman' hut, but no one was to move in until the tall Englishman was seen. Chauvelin threatened to kill any soldier who made a move before the Scarlet Pimpernel arrived.

It wasn't very long until the group was within sight of the hut. Knowing that her husband was in grave danger, Marguerite made a run for the hut. She was desperate to warn the men inside, for the could then escape and warn Sir Percy. Marguerite slipped and fell down. Chauvelin heard the noise (DO). He [sent] one of his soldiers after her. Before she could reach the hut, Marguerite was caught. The soldier took her (DO) to Chauvelin. He told her that one of the men in the hut was her brother. If she cooperated, her brother would be set free. If she didn't, all of the men in the hut would be killed.

Edit this passage from *The Scarlet Pimpernel*.

There are 10 errors in this passage.

Chauvelin was determined to catch the Scarlet Pimpernel, and he would not allow Lady Blakeney to destroy his plans. Knowing Marguerite would not risk her brother's life, he left her alone. He had the Jewish man bound and gagged to ensure that he wouldn't make any noise.

Marguerite felt absolutely helpless. She dreaded the arrival of her husband, the Scarlet Pimpernel. His death seemed unstoppable!

Suddenly they heard a man singing. Recognizing her husband's voice, Marguerite cried out a warning. She was thrown roughly to the ground and silenced. The singing stopped. Chauvelin ordered his men to storm the hut and kill everyone inside. The soldiers charged into the hut, but no shots were fired. There was no one inside! The soldiers explained that they had seen the men slip out of the hut some time before. Because Chauvelin had ordered them to wait until the tall Englishman arrived, they hadn't attacked (they / them). Chauvelin was outraged, but it was true. He had told the men they would be killed if they moved before the Scarlet Pimpernel arrived; they had obeyed.

Edit this passage from *The Scarlet Pimpernel*.

There are 15 errors in this passage.

Chauvelin and the soldiers quickly moved out to search the beach for the singer and the escaped aristocrats. Marguerite was left alone with the Jew. She wondered if her husband and brother were safely out of France.

As the soldiers disappeared from sight, Marguerite heard her husband's voice! Confused, she looked around. He spoke again, and Marguerite whirled to face the Jewish man. It was Sir Percy! His clever disguise had fooled Chauvelin and his own wife! After hearing Chauvelin's strict orders, Percy had freed himself from his bindings. Then he had crept up to the hut and slipped a note inside. The note instructed the men to go down the beach to where a boat was hidden. Percy had waited a while and then started singing loudly. No one had suspected the old Jew, and the men had escaped to safety. Sir Percy had also told them to send a boat back for Lady Blakeney and (himself / themselves), and it was on its way. Marguerite [fell] into her husband's arms. Gazing into his eyes, Marguerite saw that they were filled with love.

The daring Scarlet Pimpernel had succeeded once again!

Edit this passage from *The Time Machine*.

There are 14 errors in this passage.

I sat with a handful of other men at a friend's table. He had invited us to supper this fine Thursday evening in order to share his latest experiment with us. He warned us that what he was about to say contradicted some of the principles we had been taught in school. When he finished his explanation, we sat shocked. He claimed to have invented a machine that could travel through time!

Our friend, we'll call him the Time Traveller, disappeared into his lab and returned with a small model. It had a seat, levers, knobs, and many other tiny parts. The Time Traveller told us that it was a working model of his time machine. He asked one of the men to push one of the little levers, and the machine began to quiver. Then it disappeared! The Time Traveller insisted that it had traveled into the future. We didn't believe that it had really traveled through time, but there was no other explanation.

65

Circle the correct words in the sentences below.

I live in a (good / well) neighborhood. It's (among / between) two parks.

The article (implied / inferred) that girls read more (than / then) boys.

The case required (farther / further) investigation.

The caffeine had an (affect / effect) for a while, but (than / then) I slept.

66

Edit this passage from *The Time Machine*.

There are 13 errors in this passage.

I went back to the Time Traveller's house one week later. Several men (was / were) sitting at the supper table. I sat down (among / between) them. Only one of the men had been there the previous week. The Time Traveller was not at the table. We began to talk about where he might be.

The door opened. In limped the Time Traveller. He was covered with dust and dirt, and he looked pale and exhausted. He motioned for something to drink. One of the men handed him a glass of water. The Time Traveller gulped it down and (than / then) filled his plate with food. He told us that he had a (good / well) story to tell, but he had to satisfy his immense hunger first. We watched him curiously.

"Just one question," I begged. "Have you been time traveling?"

"I have," he answered. His serious response did not (imply / infer) that he was joking.

The Time Traveller began to eat while the rest of us exchanged doubtful, questioning glances. We didn't question him (farther / further). When he had finished eating, we retired to a [more comfortable] room. Then he began his story.

67

Edit this passage from *The Time Machine*.

There are 10 errors in this passage.

He had finished the time machine that very morning. He climbed onto the seat, pulled the starting lever, and then quickly pulled the stopping lever. In just that short amount of time, he noted from the clock that several hours had passed. The Time Traveller pulled the starting lever again. The machine started to whirl and shake as time slipped by faster and faster. He watched his surroundings change as the years flew by. When he finally pulled the stopping lever, he was [thrown] from the machine. Disoriented, he stood up and looked around. He was in a grassy field. A large statue loomed nearby. There (was / were) a handful of gigantic buildings (farther / further) off in the distance. It was very warm outside, and everything looked calm and peaceful. Checking one of the dials on the time machine, the Time Traveller noted that it was the year 802701. (Than / Then) he [took] the levers off the machine and put them in his pocket for safekeeping. As he continued to scan the landscape, he saw several [people] approaching (he / him).

68

Edit this passage from *The Time Machine*.

There are 13 errors in this passage.

  The Time Traveller was struck by their strange appearance. The people were about four feet tall and were clothed in colorful robes. They (was / were) very beautiful but also very frail. The thing that surprised the Time Traveller the most was that they showed no signs of fear. Instead, they laughed when they saw him and chattered loudly to one another. He could not understand their language, but they seemed very friendly.

  The Time Traveller followed the little people into one of the big buildings. It was beautifully constructed but obviously very old and worn. There were tables filled with all kinds of strange fruit. The little people [sat] down on cushions and began to eat. The Time Traveller joined them, and he began to try and learn their language. Although this amused the people for a while, they soon became bored and simply ignored him. He did, however, manage to learn that they were called Eloi.

  The Time Traveller was disappointed. He had expected the people of the future to be brilliant. Instead, the Eloi seemed more like [children].

69

Edit this passage from *The Time Machine*.

There are 12 errors in this passage.

  After the Time Traveller finished eating, he went back outside to explore. As (he / him) thought about these people of the future, h realized what had happened. Man had become so accustomed to adapting the world to his needs that there was no longer anything t worry about or fear. Without the need for strength, the (affect / effect) was that man had become weak. The Eloi simply led such comfortable [lives] that they had no reason to be anything but happy, thoughtless children.

  After reaching this conclusion, the Time Traveller returned to the field where he had first arrived. The time machine was gone! Frantic, he searched for any sign of the machine. He had taken the levers off, so he knew it had only been moved. There were tracks in the grass leading to the giant statue. Rapping on the panels in the base, the Time Traveller realized that it was hollow. It was easy to figure out that the time machine had been put inside of the statue, but who had done it? He tried to open the panels; they wouldn't budge.

70

Modifiers

Rewrite the sentences below so that the meanings are clear. Answers will vary.

There is a restaurant next to the gas station that serves wonderful food.

There is a restaurant that serves wonderful food next to the gas station.

After singing many Christmas carols, my eyes were droopy.

My eyes were droopy after I sang many Christmas carols.

Watching through the window, the birds gathered at the feeder.

He watched through the window as the birds gathered at the feeder.

She told her daughter to lift the glass vase with two hands.

She told her daughter to use two hands to lift the glass vase.

Driving home from the store, the baby remained asleep.

The baby remained asleep as her mother drove home from the store.

71

Edit this passage from *The Time Machine*. Find and underline one misplaced modifier and one dangling modifier.

There are 10 errors in this passage.

  It didn't take very long for the Time Traveller to realize that there was something the Eloi feared. They were terrified of the dark. As soon as the sun set, they all went inside for the night. They slept in large groups in the buildings all huddled together.

  The Time Traveller [woke] up early one morning. It was still dark outside. Feeling restless, he went outside to watch the sun rise. In the first rays of light, (he / him) saw several human-like creatures scurrying across the ground. He tried to follow one. It did have some characteristics of a person, but it was not beautiful like the Eloi. It was very pale, had large gray eyes and light hair, and moved with surprising speed and agility. It entered what looked like a well and disappeared from view. Peering down the shaft, the darkness had already hidden the small creature. Only his large eyes (was / were) visible in the oppressive blackness.

72

108

Edit this passage from *The Time Machine*.

There are 12 errors in this passage.

The Time Traveller was puzzled about the pale creatures. He learned from the Eloi that they were called Morlocks. The Eloi spoke of them with shivers and fearful glances, and they refused to go near any of the openings to the underground. The Time Traveller realized that the Morlocks lived underground and [came] out only at night.

It didn't take very long for the Time Traveller to reach a new conclusion. The Eloi were the descendants of the richer class of people. They now enjoyed a comfortable lifestyle and had no memory of work. They had become weak, mindless people. The Morlocks (was / were) the descendants of the common laborers. They had been the people who toiled away in large mines and underground railways. As time went by, they had spent more and more time working in underground [factories]. Over time they had become so accustomed to the dark that they could no longer live in the light. They had become strong people who worked and ruled the dark.

73

Edit this passage from *The Time Machine*.

There are 10 errors in this passage.

The Time Traveller felt sure that the Morlocks had put the time machine in the base of the statue. When he questioned the Eloi about the statue, they ran away in disgust. The Time Traveller had no choice. If he wanted to find his way back home, he had to go into the underground world of the Morlocks.

Two days passed before he worked up the courage to climb down into the shaft. The Time Traveller gathered his strength and started down the dark passage. He could hear deep voices and the hum of machinery. When he got to the bottom, he felt the Morlocks pressing in around him. He lit a match, and they ran away from the light. As soon as the match burned out, they crept up to him again. The dark, heavy atmosphere seemed to close in around him. The Morlocks grabbed at his clothing. He lit another match; they fled for a second time. Realizing he was out of matches, the Time Traveller turned to leave. He climbed out of reach just before the Morlocks could drag him (farther / further) into their underground world.

74

Edit this passage from *The Time Machine*.

There are 14 errors in this passage.

The Time Traveller's only hope was to break into the base of the statue. He explored more of the Eloi's world in search of something he could use to pry open the panels. After finding an iron crowbar, he returned to the statue. Surprisingly, the panels were open. The Time Traveller saw his time machine sitting inside. The Morlocks were trying to trap him!

Fingering the levers in his pocket, the Time Traveller stepped inside the statue. As he approached the time machine, the panels slid shut behind him. He could hear the evil giggles of the Morlocks as they [crept] towards him. The Time Traveller worked in the dark as quickly as he could to refasten the levers to the time machine. He climbed on to the machine as the Morlocks surrounded him. (They / Them) grabbed and pulled at his clothes, and he fought with all of his strength to stay on the machine. He pulled the starting lever. The machine whirred to life, and he [felt] the Morlocks' hands fall away.

75

Labeling Sentences

In the sentences below, underline the subjects once and the verbs twice. Circle the adjectives. Mark the adverbs (ADV), the direct objects (DO), and the indirect objects (IO). Cross out any prepositional phrases.

ADV   IO   DO
I secretly bought my older sister a new necklace for her birthday.

Inside the pen, the five little pigs wallowed in the mud.

        ADV
Cadence is happily playing with her toys on the floor.

        DO
Jordan scored two points during the first half of the basketball game.

76

109

Edit this passage from *The Time Machine*.

There are 11 errors in this passage.

The Time Traveller set the dials on the machine to return home. He traveled back into the past at an incredible speed. He watched time pass in reverse until (he / him) recognized the world once again. He slowed his speed, and eventually he saw the familiar sight of his own laboratory. He carefully pulled the stopping lever. When he climbed off, he heard our voices in the dining room. Feeling exhausted and weak, he joined us for supper.

That was the end of the Time Traveller's story. It was a fantastic tale, but we could hardly accept it as truth! We didn't know what to think.

I returned to the Time Traveller's house the very next day to ask more questions. Just as I opened the door to his laboratory, I heard a sound like a strong, sharp wind. I seemed to see just a trace of the Time Traveller on his time machine before it vanished. I have been waiting for years, and the Time Traveller has yet to return.

Edit this passage from *Great Expectations*.

There are 17 errors in this passage.

When Pip, whose Christian name was Philip, was just seven year old, something happened that changed his life forever. He was visiting the graves of his parents and brothers when a dirty, rough man grabbed him by the shoulders. The man had an iron shackle on one of his legs. He was an escaped prisoner, and he ordered Pip to come back the next day with some food and a file. Pip was terrified of the man and his threats! He agreed and ran home as quickly as he could.

Pip lived by the [marshes] with his sister, Mrs. Joe Gargery, and her husband, Mr. Joe Gargery. Joe was a blacksmith and was not well-educated, but he was always kind to Pip. Mrs. Joe, on the other hand, constantly complained about having the additional burden of Pip. She ruled the household and was quick to punish Pip for any fault, no matter how slight.

The next day Pip stole some food out of the pantry, took a file from Joe's shop, and ran through the marshes to meet the prisoner. After giving him the items, Pip went home. He knew he'd be in trouble when Mrs. Joe discovered the missing food.

Edit this passage from *Great Expectations*.

There are 15 errors in this passage.

Pip waited nervously for Mrs. Joe to realize that some of the food was gone. It was Christmas, and they had company over. Just as she discovered a missing pie, there was a knock on the door. It was a group of soldiers! Pip thought they had come for him, but the sergeant was looking for Joe. He needed a pair of handcuffs fixed, for they were going after the escaped prisoner.

After mending the handcuffs, Joe and Pip went with the soldiers to find the prisoner. As they got closer and closer to the marshes, they heard two [men] yelling. Following the noise, they came upon two prisoners. They (was / were) fighting. The prisoner Pip had met explained that he was determined not to let the other prisoner escape. Even though it prevented him from escaping, he wanted to make sure the soldiers caught the other prisoner. He didn't say anything to Pip; he told the soldiers he'd stolen food from the blacksmith's house. Joe was stunned, and Pip was relieved.

Edit this passage from *Great Expectations*.

There are 13 errors in this passage.

One day Mrs. Joe came home with some surprising news. Pip was to go to Miss Havisham's house the very next day. Miss Havisham was a rich, mysterious lady who lived in a large house. Pip was not looking forward to the trip, but Mrs. Joe was thrilled. She thought that if Pip pleased the old woman, Miss Havisham would give them some money.

When Pip arrived at Miss Havisham's house, a pretty girl named Estella opened the door. She led him to Miss Havisham's room. Pip entered and looked around. Miss Havisham was a pale, old woman. She hadn't been outside for many years, and she wore a wedding gown that was yellow with age. An old, mouse-eaten wedding cake sat on a table. Everything in the room (was / were) covered in cobwebs. The clocks were all stopped at the same time. Miss Havisham wanted Pip to entertain her. He didn't quite know what to do, so she ordered him to play cards with Estella.

Pip went back to Miss Havisham's house many times to keep the old woman company. Estella always treated him badly, but Pip admired (she / her) anyway.

Diagramming Sentences

Diagram the sentences below.

My best friend often wears her blue sweater.

Those kids are playing football in the mud.

A noisy bird is chirping loudly outside my bedroom window.

The doctor wrote him a prescription on yellow paper.

She slowly handed me the crossword puzzle from the newspaper.

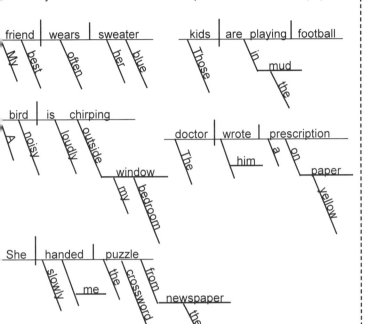

81

Edit this passage from *Great Expectations*.

There are 13 errors in this passage.

A year or so later Pip was old enough to be apprenticed to Joe. Miss Havisham gave Joe some money for Pip's services and told Pip he no longer needed to come and visit her. Although Pip had dreamed of the day he would start his apprenticeship, he was no longer excited. Estella had made Pip realize that he was common; he was now ashamed of the simple trade. Every day he worried that Estella would see him working and covered with soot.

Pip now went to see Miss Havisham just once a year. Estella had gone abroad to study, and Miss Havisham took an odd sort of delight in the fact that Pip missed her. Pip worked for Joe for many years, and he thought of Estella more as time passed. He was determined to become a gentleman in order to gain Estella's love. Pip shared his feelings with Biddy, the girl who helped Mrs. Joe around the house. Biddy, who was kind and sensible, told Pip he shouldn't have to change in order to win love. Pip wished he could love Biddy instead, but his heart had been captured by Estella.

82

Edit this passage from *Great Expectations*.

There are 14 errors in this passage.

One Saturday night a man approached Joe and Pip. Pip recognized the man as someone he'd seen many years ago at Miss Havisham's house. The man introduced himself as Mr. Jaggers. He was a lawyer and had brought news for Pip. An anonymous benefactor had taken an interest in Pip. The common boy had come into a great fortune and was to be educated as a gentleman! There were two conditions. Pip (was / were) to keep the name of Pip, and the benefactor was to remain a mystery until he or she decided to reveal his or her identity. Mr. Jaggers also offered Joe some money, for he would be losing Pip's help. Joe refused. Pip's dreams had come true! He was going to be a gentleman! Mr. Jaggers told him that he would leave for London at once to start his education. Matthew Pocket, one of Miss Havisham's relatives, was going to be his tutor. Even though his benefactor wished to remain a mystery, Pip (implied / inferred) that it was Miss Havisham.

83

Edit this passage from *Great Expectations*.

There are 12 errors in this passage.

Within a few days Pip became somewhat arrogant. He was ashamed of Joe's simple, uneducated ways and was eager to begin his life as a gentleman in London.

Once in London Pip [found] his way to the office of Mr. Jaggers. The lawyer explained that Pip could get money from him and that Pip had credit all over town to buy whatever he needed. Pip would be staying at the inn with Matthew Pocket's son for a few days before going to Matthew's house.

The son's name was Herbert. Pip had seen him once at Miss Havisham's many years ago when they were both young boys. Herbert and Pip became great friends, and Herbert told Pip everything he knew about his mysterious relative. Miss Havisham had been swindled by a man who had pretended to love her. She had loved him deeply and had [given] him a lot of money. On the day of their wedding, he had never come. She had [worn] her wedding dress and stayed inside ever since. Miss Havisham had adopted Estella and raised (she / her) to break men's hearts.

84

Edit this passage from *Great Expectations*.

There are 16 errors in this passage.

Pip settled into his new lifestyle. He spent some of his time with Matthew Pocket being educated, but he continued to live with Herbert at the inn. While Pip had money to spend, Herbert did not. Both boys [spent] much more (than / then) they could afford and ran up steep debts.

Mrs. Joe died some time later; Pip went home for her funeral. Not long afterwards Pip turned twenty-one. He expected to find out the name of his benefactor, but Mr. Jaggers merely handed him an envelope filled with money. From now on Pip would receive a set amount of money each year, and Mr. Jaggers would no longer be involved. Pip used the money to secretly secure a (good / well) job for Herbert.

A couple of weeks after Pip turned twenty-three, there was a knock on the door. Being alone in the house, Pip answered the door. It was the prisoner from his childhood! The man entered the house and began talking. Pip was horrified. (Than / Then) the man said that he was Pip's benefactor!

85

Combine each group of sentences below into one sentence. Answers will vary.

I like chili. It is my favorite meal. It is perfect on a cold day.
My favorite meal, chili, is perfect on a cold day.

He read three books. They were big books. The books were about wars. It took him two weeks.
He read three big books about wars in two weeks.

The farmer planted corn. He also planted beans. He planted an acre of each. The farmer planted them two months ago.
The farmer planted an acre of beans and an acre of corn two months ago.

The baby had big blue eyes. She also had blonde hair. The baby was smiling. She had three little teeth.
The smiling baby had big blue eyes, blonde hair, and three little teeth.

I share a bedroom with my sister. She is older than me. Her name is Bethany.
I share a bedroom with my older sister, Bethany.

86

Edit this passage from *Great Expectations*.

There are 14 errors in this passage.

The man's name was Magwitch, and he told his story to Pip. He had been in and out of jail for most of his life. He had never forgotten Pip's kindness in bringing him food years ago. After serving that particular sentence, Magwitch had decided that he would work hard and give all of his money to Pip. He knew that he could never be more than a common fellow, but he took pride in knowing that he was making a gentleman.

Pip did not feel the least bit grateful. He had thought he was being aided by Miss Havisham, not some dirty criminal!

Through conversations with Magwitch, Herbert, Mr. Jaggers, and Miss Havisham, Pip was finally able to piece together the mystery surrounding Estella. Mr. Jaggers' housekeeper had been the wife of Magwitch. She had committed a crime, and then she'd disappeared from Magwitch's life along with their young daughter. Mr. Jaggers had helped the woman stay out of jail and had sent her daughter to live with Miss Havisham. Magwitch was Estella's father!

87

112

Edit this passage from *Great Expectations*.

There are 14 errors in this passage.

Pip and Herbert discovered another bit of news after hearing Magwitch's story. He had once worked for a man by the name of Compeyson, the very same man who had swindled Miss Havisham. Magwitch and Compeyson had both been arrested, but Compeyson made sure the evidence fell more heavily upon Magwitch. Compeyson was also a very well-bred man, a fact which had helped him get a [shorter] prison term than Magwitch. When Pip and the soldiers had found Magwitch long ago, it was Compeyson whom Magwitch had been holding.

Although Magwitch was very pleased with his success in creating a gentleman, Pip secretly decided that he would spend no more of the money.

Magwitch's life was in danger now that he had come back to London. He had been sent overseas and was not supposed to ever return. Knowing Magwitch would not leave him, Pip and Herbert devised a plan to get both Magwitch and Pip out of London safely.

Meanwhile, Estella had married a brutish man out of boredom. She hadn't married for love, for Miss Havisham had never shown her what love was.

88

Edit this passage from *Great Expectations*.

There are 16 errors in this passage.

Pip was being watched; he knew that Compeyson and the authorities were trying to find Magwitch. (He / Him) and Herbert did their best to figure out a (good / well) way to get Pip's benefactor out of England. When the day came, Pip and Herbert picked up Magwitch by boat. He wore a long cloak and seemed content just to be in Pip's company. Just before reaching a steamer bound for Germany, a boat full of officers overtook them. Compeyson was in the boat; he had led the officers to Magwitch. Both Magwitch and Compeyson [fell] overboard in the confusion that followed. Only Magwitch came back to the surface. He had two broken ribs and a punctured lung from hitting the side of the boat, but he was arrested anyway.

Magwitch wasn't upset about going back to prison. He was happy just to have seen the gentleman he'd made out of Pip. As for Pip, he gained respect for Magwitch and his deep generosity. He did not tell his benefactor that all of Magwitch's money and property would now be seized by the state, leaving Pip poor once again.

89

Edit this passage from *Great Expectations*.

There are 19 errors in this passage.

Magwitch was sentenced to death, but his [injuries] were so serious that it was clear he wouldn't live to be executed. Pip stayed by his side and [held] his hand as much as he could. Magwitch died happy; he had succeeded in making a gentleman and knew that his daughter was alive.

After Magwitch's death Pip became quite ill. He was in so much debt that he was arrested, but Pip fainted at that very moment. When he woke up, Joe was taking care of him. Pip felt deeply ashamed for the way he'd treated Joe. One morning Pip awoke to find that Joe had left. There was a note along with a receipt on the table. Joe had paid all of Pip's bills before returning home!

Pip went to work with Herbert, who was now a successful businessman. While Pip never became rich, he did quite (good / well) and was very happy. Many years later he returned home to visit. Joe and Biddy (was / were) married and had two children, one of whom was a son named Pip. Estella was also back in town. Her husband had died some years ago. She told Pip that she hoped (they / them) could finally be friends.

90

113